NEGROES IN SCIENCE:

NATURAL SCIENCE DOCTORATES,
1876 - 1969

James M. Jay
Wayne State University
Detroit, Michigan

BALAMP PUBLISHING
Box 7390
Detroit, Michigan 48202

L. C. No. 74-28394

First Printing, 7/71; Second Printing, 1/73

Printed in the United States.

Balamp Publishing
7430 Second Avenue
Detroit, Michigan 48202

8-8-73

Dedicated to My Father on His 82nd Birthday

Table of Contents

List of Tables

List of Illustrations

Preface

This book is based on the findings of a study which the author initiated around 1958 while a member of the faculty of Southern University, Baton Rouge, Louisiana. During this time, Louisiana state law prevented Southern University from hiring whites for its faculty. State law also barred the admission of white students to the university. Because of the need to maintain a minimum percentage of doctorates on the faculty for accreditation purposes, department chairmen and other members of the faculty constantly sought to recruit doctorate holders. The constant search for new faculty recruits kept interested parties in touch with those who were advanced in their graduate studies. The author's initial list of names of Negro science doctorate recipients was begun at this time and continued to grow. The roster of names on which this study is based was obtained over a 12-year period with the help of many individuals among whom are those listed below.

The report that follows is essentially factual in nature. I have avoided making frequent comparisons of the studied subjects to their white counterparts except in those instances where the comparisons are thought to be of meaningful significance. It is the author's estimate that approximately 650 American Negroes obtained doctorate degrees in the natural sciences between 1876 and 1969, and this study is based upon data on 587 of this estimated number. Depending upon how one views the matter, this number is either extremely low or high. It is low when one considers that over 84,000 natural science doctorates were awarded by American universities between 1920-1962. On the other hand, it is a high number when one considers the adversities which the American Negro has had to endure over the years, especially in the area of higher education. While over 50 percent of the Negro population still resides in the south, it was not until fairly recently that Negroes could pursue graduate education at the doctorate degree-granting institutions nearest them. While similar institutions outside of the south have for

many years maintained an open door policy to Negro
scholars, not all of these institutions made Negroes
seeking science doctorates welcome. Whether one
views the estimated number of 650 to be high of low,
it is, nevertheless, a realistic figure and one that
must be contended with. It is the hope of the author
that this study may in various ways shed more light
upon this segment of the national scientific pool and
open up more ways in which more members of this
ethnic minority may contribute to the science doctorate pool of this country.

I am grateful to a large number of individuals
who aided me in obtaining the names and addresses of
many of the scientists in this study. I am particular-
ly grateful to the following: Dr. W. M. Banks of Howard
Univ., Dr. R. W. Brown of Tuskegee Inst., Dr. W. E.
Byrd of Lincoln Univ. (Mo.), Dr. O. R. Collins of the
Univ. of Calif. (Berkeley), Dr. W. Douglass of Inland
Steel Corp., Dr. R. H. Dunn of Va. State College, Dr.
L. Frederick of Atlanta Univ., Dr. M. Gipson, Jr., of
Va. State College, Mrs. C. L. Golightly of Detroit,
Dr. H. A. Hill of the Riverside Res. Lab. (Haverhill,
Mass.), Dr. W. H. Jones of San Francisco State College,
Mrs. D. R. Kellon of Cleveland, Dr. C. E. King of
Tenn. A & I Univ., Dr. J. R. Lawson of Fisk Univ., Dr.
C. E. Monroe of Morgan State College, and Dr. W.
Moore of Southern Univ.

I am also grateful to Dr. A. R. Padgett of Esso
Corp., Dr. B. Peery of Indiana Univ., Dr. J. J.
Prestage of Southern Univ., Dr. J. P. Rier of Rutgers
Univ., Dr. R. B. Sanders of the Univ. of Kansas, Dr.
T. R. Sherrod of the Univ. of Ill. Med. School, Dr.
L. B. Stephens, Jr. of Calif. State College (Long
Beach), Dr. J. H. Wallace of Ohio State Univ., Dr. B.
Watson of Tuskegee Inst., and Dr. J. D. Withers of
Clark College.

I thank Dr. C. L. Golightly, Associate Dean of
the College of Liberal Arts at Wayne State Univ. for
reading and criticizing the entire manuscript. I owe
a special debt of gratitude to Dr. L. R. Harmon and
Dr. F. D. Boercker of the Office of Scientific
Personnel, National Academy of Sciences, National
Research Council for providing me with some invaluable
statistical data on many of the subjects in this study.

Lastly, I would like to thank Miss Robbie J. DeVaull and Miss Lois E. Mustonen, the former for assisting me in compiling pertinent data, and the latter for her expert assistance in typing drafts of the manuscript and the final manuscript in its present form.

James M. Jay
Detroit, Michigan
1971

1

Introduction

In 1866, Yale University became the first American educational institution to confer the Ph.D. degree. Ten years later, this same University became the first American University to confer this degree upon an American Negro. This person was Edward Alexander Bouchet who was awarded the degree in physics and who, while at Yale, became the first American Negro to become a member of Phi Beta Kappa (Greene, 1946). While Bouchet received the Ph.D. in 1876, only one other American Negro was to be awarded this degree in the sciences by the year 1900 (A. O. Coffin, 1889).

In his study of Negro recipients of doctorate degrees from 1876 to 1943 in all areas, Greene (1946) uncovered 119 individuals who received science doctorates. Figure 1-1 presents by years the Negro science doctorate recipients in the present study from 1876 through 1969. It may be noted that only 13 persons had been awarded science doctorates prior to 1930. The drop in numbers of recipients for the years 1945-1948 may be attributed to the reduction in the number of college graduates during the early years of World War II. Except for the years prior to and including 1943, it is doubtful whether all relevant individuals have been identified. This is especially true for the years 1967, 1968, and 1969. Great difficulty has been experienced in identifying these more recent graduates compared to the older ones.

The years in which the doctorate recipients earned their undergraduate degrees are presented in Figure 1-2. It may be noted that the number of undergraduate degree recipients during the late 50's and early 60's is sharply lower than for the late 40's.

1

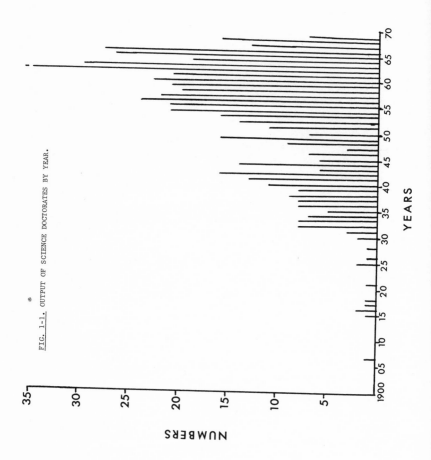

FIG. 1-1. OUTPUT OF SCIENCE DOCTORATES BY YEAR.

NUMBERS

YEARS

2

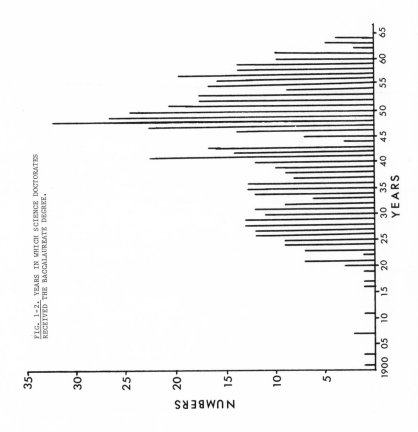

FIG. 1-2. YEARS IN WHICH SCIENCE DOCTORATES RECEIVED THE BACCALAUREATE DEGREE.

3

On the assumption that this decrease is not real, this may be taken to simply indicate that the number of doctorate recipients which would have received undergraduate degrees during these times are among those who were not uncovered in these searches. The average time between undergraduate and doctorate degrees by the individuals in this study is approximately 10 years. It should be noted that World War II veterans probably account for the high undergraduate output during the late 40's. The availability of G.I. benefits to both World War II and Korean Conflict veterans is undoubtedly reflected by the high output of doctorates during the early 60's.

The precise number of American Negroes who have received science doctorates is not known. This task is made all the more difficult by the fact that doctorate degree-granting institutions by and large do not maintain ethnic identifications as parts of records. The present study is based upon 587 persons who received science doctorates between 1876 and 1969. On hand but not included are 27 other persons on whom verification of the doctorate degree could not be made but who were reported by at least one person as holding a science doctorate. While the precise number of doctorate recipients is not known over the period in question, an estimate of around 650 seems reasonable. This estimated number is substantiated by record of the National Academy of Sciences (Harmon and Soldz, 1963) from which it was determined that 351 science doctorates received baccalaureate degrees from 55 predominately Negro institutions for the period 1920-1961. When the eight doctorates awarded prior to 1920 and the 10 from foreign universities (not included in NAS statistics) are added to the 351, the total is brought to 369. On the assumption that an average of 30 degrees per year were awarded over the eight-year period 1962-1969, the total comes to 609. The difference between 609 and 650 is thought to be accounted for by discrepancies in the number of doctorates for individual undergraduate schools in this study and the NAS report. While there is no way of being certain that all recipients of science doctorates up to 1966 are included, there is every reason to believe that the vast majority of

4

relevant individuals have been included with the exception of certain discrepancies as noted above.

As previously stated, it is reasonable to assume that some of the 1967, 1968, and 1969 recipients are not included. While Greene uncovered 119 science doctorates in his study and presumed to have found all of those relevant to his study, the present study turned up 7 additional persons not included in his study but who received science doctorates during the period covered by his study. Of these 7, two received the doctorate in 1941, two in 1942, and three in 1943. Of the 119 science doctorate recipients included in Greene's study, this number represented 33.1 percent of the total of Ph.D.'s uncovered by him. Assuming that the ratio of 1:2 of science Ph.D. recipients to Ph.D. recipients in other areas is still valid, this suggests that approximately 2,000 American Negroes have been granted the Ph.D. degree, a number which is not inconsistent with recent estimates made by several University and College presidents. When Ed.D. and other doctorate recipients are added, the number approaches 3,000 or more.

IDENTIFICATION OF SUBJECTS

The book published in 1946 by Greene which included relevant individuals through 1943 provided an indispensable source of names. All science doctorate recipients included in Greene's book are included in this study. In addition, Taylor's book (1955) as well as Leaders in American Education, "Ebony" Magaxine, "Chemical and Engineering News", and several other publications which carry pictures of their subjects have been employed as sources of relevant persons. I am highly indebted to a large number of individuals who examined the list of names at various stages during its growth and provided many names as well as corrections in terms of ethnic identities (see Preface for partial list of contributors).

In no instances were colleges or universities contacted for their lists of relevant graduates. This approach was ruled out due to the generally poor response that one gets from such queries and also because of the general lack of ethnic identifications maintained by colleges and universities. While

queries could have been sent to the predominantly
Negro colleges and universities, this would have
introduced a bias in favor of these institutions.
Consequently, the data herein are not thought to
represent a bias in the direction of either colleges
or universities, geographic areas of the country,
degree areas, or sex of recipients.

Once names of prospective subjects were obtained,
a search of published biographies was made for
pertinent data. Individuals who had published
biographies were not contacted for any additional
data. A brief questionnaire was sent to those who
were not published (see appendix). On many of those
who did not respond to the questionnaire, their names
(along with others) were submitted to the Division
of Personnel, National Academy of Sciences (NAS),
National Research Council. This body maintains files
on all U.S. citizens who receive doctorates at
American institutions. The NAS files go back to 1920.
Not only was the degree status confirmed but other
data pertaining to undergraduate and graduate origins
and degree fields were also obtained. On individuals
who received the doctorate since 1957, the state of
birth was also provided by the above agency. While
not all 587 persons in this study were verified in
this manner, their degree status was verified either
by direct contact with individuals known to the
author or these persons were generally considered by
their places of employment as having received a
doctorate degree in their claimed fields.

DEGREE AREAS REPRESENTED

Of the 587 persons in this study, all but four
hold the Ph.D. degree in one of the biological,
medical, physical, pharmaceutical, or agricultural
sciences. Recipients of the degree in psychology
and anthropology are not included. Of the four
persons who do not hold the Ph.D. degree, two were
recipients of the Sc.D. and two the Dr. P.H. degrees.
These are included here as being roughly equivalent
to the Ph.D. degree, having been awarded in one of
the pure sciences. Holders of the M.D., D.D.S., or
D.V.M. degrees solely are not included.

The 587 subjects in this study are composed of
529 or 90 percent males and 58 or 10 percent females.

6

With respect to degree fields, 42.9 percent obtained
the doctorate in the bio-sciences, 31.7 percent in
chemistry, 16 percent in the physical sciences other
than chemistry, 6.5 percent in the agricultural
sciences, and 2.9 percent in the pharmaceutical
sciences (Fig. 1-3). At least 22 of these persons
hold M.D. degrees in addition to science doctorates,
while at least 2 hold the D.V.M. and at least 2 the
D.D.S. degrees. Double-doctorate holders thus
comprise 4.4 percent of the subjects in this study
which might well be a higher percentage of double-
degree holders for this population than is the case
for the total science doctorate pool.

Only 26 of the subjects are known by the author
to be deceased. This means that approximately 95
percent of those in this study or about 86 percent of
the estimated number of all American Negroes ever to
receive doctorate degrees in the sciences were alive
during the midpart of 1970. At least 11 of these
subjects are either now or have in the past been
presidents of colleges or universities.

SUMMARY PROFILE & TRENDS

The findings presented in the following chapters
from 587 American Negroes who obtained science
doctorates between 1876 and 1969 would seem to allow
for the following brief characterization or profile
of this segment of the U.S. science doctorate pool:
The Negro science doctorate holder is a male, born
in a small southern town, most likely educated in
segregated public schools, obtained the undergraduate
degree at a predominantly Negro college or university,
obtained the doctorate in the bio-sciences (zoology
most likely) at one of the Big-10 universities, and
is employed in academic life at a predominantly
Negro college or university. He obtained his
baccalaureate degree at age 22 and the doctorate
about 10 years later. Approximately 95 percent of all
said persons are alive today. He represents about 1
percent of science doctorates nationally. Among other
aspects of this segment of the national science
doctorate pool, the following may be noted.

1. A conservative estimate of the current average yearly output of Negro science doctorates is
between 25-30. This number appears to be increasing

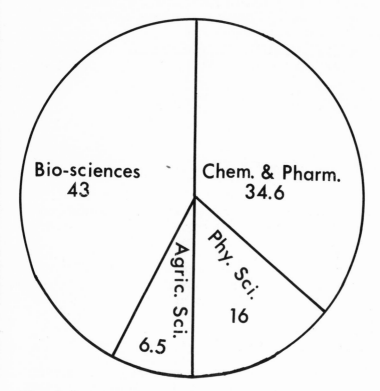

Fig. 1-3. Percent distribution of the 587 science doctorates by areas.

but not at an alarmingly high rate. While large
numbers of Negroes left the south since 1930, the
proportionate increase in science doctorate recipients
of northern origin has not taken place. The increases
are taking place in the south even at a higher rate.

2. There appears to be a slightly higher percentage of Negro females obtaining science doctorates and
this increase is more noticeable among southern-
born Negroes than their northern and western counterparts (Table 1-1).

Table 1-1. Comparison of doctorate recipients for
the periods 1876-1940, and 1960-1969 to all years.

	All years	1960-1969	1876-1940
Number of persons	587	221	90
% Southern born	75.0	79.5	60.0
% Negro undergrad.	71.8	74.7	43.5
% Private	49.9	43.0	20.0
% Big-10 doct.	37.0	30.0	30.3
% Southern doct.	4.8	10.4	0.0
% Males	90.0	88.7	95.5
% Bio-sciences	43.0	48.0	42.7
% Chemistry	31.7	33.0	29.2
% Physical sci.	16.0	14.5	22.5
% Agricultural sci.	6.5	2.3	3.4
Av. age at B.S.	22.6	22.4	22.3
Av. age at doct.	32.9	32.1	31.7
Av. no. yrs. between B.S. and doct.	10.3	9.7	9.4

3. The undergraduate origins appear to remain
about the same with the exception of the public
supported Negro colleges and universities which are
producing more science doctorates now than in earlier
years. This may be a reflection of the generally
higher salaries which these institutions can pay
compared to the private institutions, which fact may
be taken to indicate an increase in the quality of
both faculty and facilities for science teaching.
On the basis of present and past records, one of the
most effective ways of getting more Negroes into the
science doctorate pool is to strengthen and continue
to maintain the predominantly Negro colleges and
universities.

4. The pattern of doctorate universities is changing with the Big-10 universities becoming gradually less conspicuous. As the years go on, it appears that more and more Negroes will turn to the once racially segregated universities of the south for science doctorates. Also, Howard University has emerged as one of the leading producers of Negro science doctorates within the past 10 years. The institution of Ph.D. programs in the sciences by other predominantly Negro institutions (e.g., Atlanta University) may also be expected to become a significant factor in the future.

5. The academic areas in which Negroes have taken science doctorates appears to be changing only slightly, the most significant being in the agricultural sciences where, on the average, a three-fold decrease in the percentage of degree recipients occurred in the last 10 years compared to all years represented in this study (Table 1-2). The abundance

Table 1-2. Comparison of doctorate degree areas to certain aspects of origins of doctorate recipients.

	Bio-sci.	Chem. & Pharm.	Phy. Sci.	Agric.	All Areas
Number	252	203	94	38	587
% of total	43.0	34.6	16.0	6.5	100
% Southern born	81.0	68.5	67.9	96.0	75
% B.S. Negro Col.	71.4	69.0	54.0	86.5	71.8
% Private	50.0	50.0	66.7	28.0	50
% Big-10 doctorate	43.0	27.6	30.0	59.4	37
% Males	86.1	92.1	93.6	100.0	90
% Teaching Inst.	88.6	66.2	80.7	94.6	79.6

of Negroes in the bio-sciences is most likely a reflection of several related phenomena. First of all, college instruction in these fields is generally less expensive than in the physical sciences. Second, the existence of relatively large numbers of doctorates in this area tends to be self-perpetuating in that college students who go on for graduate work are very often influenced to do so by their professors. Third, high school instruction in the bio-sciences tends to be of a higher level than that for other sciences. Fourth, it has been found that more bio-science doctorates come from high schools with small graduating classes than physical science doctorates (Harmon, 1961). Most southern-born Negroes graduate in relatively small high school classes. While there are other possible explanations for the general preponderance of bio-scientists among Negroes, these four appear the more attractive. The relatively low numbers of Negroes in the physical sciences may reflect the greater costs involved in college instructions in these areas, the general lack of a sufficient number of qualified instructors, etc. Harmon (1961) has pointed out that the physical sciences are more sensitive to high school class size than all other areas. This appears to be related to the generally better position of large high schools of being able to provide the necessary facilities for instruction in these areas. In the case of areas such as astronomy, geology, and meteorology, very few Negro colleges offer courses in these subjects not to speak of majors or minors. The generally poorer high school preparations in mathematics throughout the south is, of course, also important in the paucity of Negroes in those areas of the physical sciences which require good preparation in this subject.

6. The average number of years between undergraduate and doctorate degrees remained about the same for the past 10 years compared to all years, the average being approximately three years longer for the subjects in this study compared to the national mean of 7.6 years for all natural science doctorates between 1920-1961 (Harmon and Soldz, 1963). The geographic origins of these subjects are presented in the next chapter.

11

2

Geographic Origins

Of the 587 scientists in this study, states of birth are known for 546. One reason for the lack of this type information on the other 41 is due in part to the fact that the National Academy of Sciences did not include states of birth in its computer files prior to 1957. In addition, this type of information is lacking for some recipients of the doctorate since 1960. The states in which these 546 persons were born are presented in Table 2-1 and Fig. 2-1. The largest number (50) was born in Texas followed by Georgia (46), Virginia and North Carolina (44 each), Alabama (41), Louisiana and South Carolina (38 each), and others. In terms of north-south origins, 75 percent of these scientists were born in the U. S. south while only 25 percent were born in the north and west. This pattern is in sharp contrast to all U.S. science doctorates for the years 1920-1961 where only 10,906 of 84,038 or about 13 percent were of southern origin (Harmon and Soldz, 1963). Thirteen were born in the Caribbean area but are included in this study because all received their doctorates in the U.S. and are generally considered in the same category as American Negroes. Table 2-1 also presents the breakdown of these individuals by state relative to their doctorate degree areas. Of the 236 persons who earned the doctorate in the bio-sciences, 81 percent were born in the south while 68 percent of the 183 chemists, 68 percent of the other physical and pharmaceutical scientists, and 96 percent of the agricultural scientists were southern born. Of possible significance is the larger number of persons in the areas of mathematics, physics, and engineering who were born in Georgia and Virginia.

Table 2-1. States and places of birth of 546 of the
587 scientists in this study along with the number of
doctoral recipients in the various disciplines for
each place of birth.

Birth place	Rank	Bio.	Chem.	Phys.	Pharm.	Agric.	Total
Texas	1	24	18	5		3	50
Georgia	2	21	13	12			46
N. C.	3	20	17	1	1	5	44
Virginia	3	22	9	8	1	4	44
Alabama	5	15	19	6	1	1	41
Louisiana	6	21	8	3	3	3	38
S. C.	6	24	8	6			38
Penn.	8	14	7	5	1		27
Missouri	9	6	6	5	1		18
D. C.	10	11	5	1			17
Mississippi	10	9	4		1	3	17
Illinois	12	4	6	6			16
Kentucky	13	3	7	4		1	15
Florida	14	4	5	3	1	1	14
Tennessee	14	5	4	2	1	2	14
New Jersey	16	3	6	3			12
New York	17	3	6	1			10
Michigan	18	2	6	1			9
Maryland	19	3	3	2			8
Oklahoma	19	2	2	2		2	8
Arkansas	21	3	1		1	2	7
Mass.	21	1	5	1			7
W. Va.	21	4	1	2			7
B. W. I.	24	3	2		1		6
Indiana	24		2	3	1		6
Kansas	26		3		1	1	5
Ohio	26	3	1	1			5
California	28		2				2
Connecticut	28	1	1				2
Jamaica	28	2					2
Iowa	-	1					1
Cuba	-		1				1
Delaware	-		1				1
Fr. W. I.	-	1					1
Minnesota	-		1				1
Panama	-		1				1
Puerto Rico	-	1					1

Table 2-1, cont'd

Nebraska	-			1			1
Virgin Is.	-		1				1
Wisconsin	-		1				1
TOTALS	-	236	183	84	15	28	546

The relative efficiency of doctorate recipient production by the states from which 4 or more scientists were born is presented in Table 2-2. The ratio of Negro science doctorates to the Negro state populations is based upon 1930 U.S. census figures. The 1930 census figures were chosen since the av. age of all scientists in this study is around 40. It can be seen from Table 2-2 that the state of Massachusetts had the lowest ratio of scientists to total state population followed by the District of Columbia, Missouri, Kansas, Kentucky, Pennsylvania, and others, down to Arkansas which had a ratio of 1 doctorate recipient to 68,352 Negroes in the state during the 1930 census count.

While 75 percent of 546 of the 587 persons over the period 1876-1969 were born in the south, it was of interest to know if the percentage of southern-born Negroes who hold the science doctorate was the same for recent years as for earlier years. Of the 587 persons in this study, 221 were awarded the doctorate since 1960 and an inspection of Table 2-3 reveals that the same general pattern of states of origin prevailed for the more recent recipients as for the total pool (see also Table 1-1, p. 9). Of the 221 persons, states of birth are known for 215. One-hundred and seventy-one or 79.5 percent were born in the south, nearly 5 percent higher than for all years. These 221 persons consist of 196 males and 25 females.

It was of interest to determine whether or not the persons born in the south remained there for high school and undergraduate studies. Some insight into this question was gained by examining the place of birth, location of high school, and geographic location of undergraduate schools of the 93 scientists whose biographies were not published but who responded to a simple questionnaire (see appendix). The data in Table 2-4 show that 78 or 84 percent of these persons were born in a southern state, the same

14

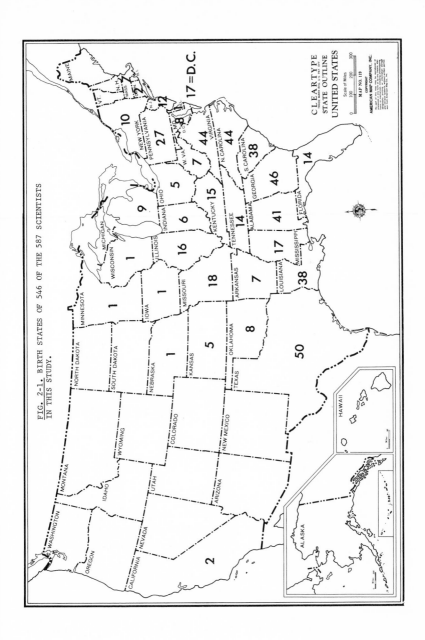

FIG. 2-1. BIRTH STATES OF 546 OF THE 587 SCIENTISTS IN THIS STUDY.

15

Table 2-2. States in which 4 or more doctorate recipients were born, the Negro census populations for 1930, and the number of science doctorates per total Negro state population.

States	No. of doct.	1930 Negro Census Pop.	Ratio of Docts. to Negro State Tot.
Mass.	7	52,365	7,481
D. C.	17	132,068	7,769
Missouri	18	223,840	12,436
Kansas	5	66,344	13,269
Kentucky	15	226,040	15,069
Penn.	27	431,257	15,973
W. Va.	7	114,893	16,413
Texas	50	854,964	17,099
New Jersey	12	208,828	17,402
Indiana	6	111,982	18,664
Michigan	9	169,453	18,828
Louisiana	38	776,326	20,430
Illinois	16	328,972	20,561
N. C.	44	918,647	20,878
New York	10	208,828	20,883
S. C.	38	793,681	20,886
Oklahoma	8	172,198	21,525
Alabama	41	944,834	23,045
Georgia	46	1,071,125	23,285
Florida	14	431,828	30,845
Tennessee	14	477,646	34,118
Maryland	8	276,379	34,547
Mississippi	17	1,009,718	59,395
Ohio	5	309,304	61,861
Arkansas	7	478,463	68,352

percentage attended and graduated from a high school in the same section of the country, and 85 percent attended a predominantly Negro college or university, also in the south. These 93 scientists represented both males and females, most all academic areas, and a wide span of years in which the terminal degree was obtained. This finding may be taken to indicate that, in general, those scientists who were born in the south received both their high school and undergraduate training there.

Table 2-3. Birth states of 215 of 221 scientists who received the doctorate between 1960 and 1969.

State	Number
Texas	26
Alabama	22
Louisiana	21
Georgia	17
South Carolina	15
North Carolian	13
Virginia	9
Florida	9
Missouri	9
Pennsylvania	8
Tennessee	8
Kentucky	6
Mississippi	6
Michigan	6
District of Columbia	5
Illinois	5
Maryland	4
New Jersey	4
West Virginia	4

Two each from the following states: New York, West Indies, Delaware, Kansas. One each from 10 other states.

Table 2-4. Place of birth, location of high school, and undergraduate origin of 93 Negro scientists whose biographies are not published and who responded to questionnaire.

Place of birth	Number	%
South	78	83.9
North	13	14.0
Location of high school		
South	78	83.9
North	13	14.0
Undergraduate origin		
Negro institution	79	85.0
Other institution	14	15.0

In regards to the cities and towns in which these scientists were born, 39 percent of 459 for whom this information was available were born in towns with 1950 census total populations below 10,000 (Table 2-5).

17

Over 60 percent were born in towns with total
populations below 100,000 while only 19 percent were
born in cities with populations of 500,000 and above.
Only 58 cities and towns produced two or more doctorate recieipents while one scientist each was born in
246 additional cities and towns (see appendix for
list of these).

Table 2-5. 1950 census total population of cities and
towns in which 459 scientists in this study were born.

Population of city or town	No. scientists	%
Below 10,000	179	39.1
10,000-24,999	43	9.4
25,000-49,999	27	5.9
50,000-99,999	50	10.9
100,000-299,999	36	7.9
300,000-499,999	35	7.6
Over 500,000	89	19.4

    The 18 largest northern cities in which scien-
tists in this study were born are listed in Table 2-6
along with the number of scientists and the 1930
Negro census population. These 62 persons represented
a ratio of 1 Negro science doctorate recipient to
21,967 Negroes in these cities in 1930. By contrast,
the 18 largest southern cities and towns from which
Negro doctorate recipients were born produced a total
of 91 persons making for a ratio of 1:12,324 (Table
2-7). It is clear from these findings that the large
northern and western cities have not produced Negro
science doctorate recipients as well as southern
cities and this topic is discussed further in Chapter
10.
    The 58 cities and towns in which two or more
scientists were born are listed in Table 2-8 along
with the 1930 Negro census population and ratio of
doctorates to total Negro population. Towns such as
Brunswick, Ga., Henderson, N.C., as well as others
have been outstanding in terms of their high ratios
of doctorates to total 1930 Negro population. This is
especially true of New Bedford, Mass., Kingstree, S.C.,
Smithville, Tex. and others presented in Table 2-8
even though only two doctorate recipients in this

18

study are known to have been born in each. Bond
(1967) has traced this degree of exceptionally high
production to usually one key high school in these
towns and generally to one or more key teachers or
principals who distinguished themselves by their
abilities to motivate and stimulate their students
to a high degree. Bond further found that a large
number of Negro doctorate holders in all degree fields
were relatives and this fact may also explain the
origin of several doctorates from small towns.

Table 2-6. Number of doctorate recipients born in
the 18 largest northern cities in this study along
with the 1930 Negro census populations of these cities.

	Number	1930 Census
Philadelphia, Pa.	11	219,599
Chicago, Ill.	7	233,903
New York City, N.Y.	7	327,706
St. Louis, Mo.	6	93,580
Pittsburgh, Pa.	5	54,983
Detroit, Mich.	4	120,066
Boston, Mass.	4	20,574
Kansas City, Mo.	4	38,574
Indianapolis, Ind.	2	43,967
Camden, N.J.	2	11,340
Atlantic City, N.J.	2	15,611
Cincinnati, O.	2	47,818
Columbus, O.	1	32,774
Oakland, Calif.	1	7,503
Buffalo, N.Y.	1	13,563
Brooklyn, N.Y.	1	68,921
Milwaukee, Wisc.	1	7,501
St. Paul, Minn.	1	4,001
TOTAL	62	1,361,984

Mean ratio of doctorate recipients to total Negro
population   1:21,967

Table 2-7. Number of doctorate recipients born in the 18 largest southern cities in this study along with the 1930 Negro censis populations of these cities.

	Number	1930 Census
Washington, D.C.	17	132,068
Houston, Tex.	12	63,337
Atlanta, Ga.	8	90,075
New Orleans, La.	7	129,632
Augusta, Ga.	6	24,190
Memphis, Tenn.	5	96,550
Birmingham, Ala.	5	99,077
Louisville, Ky.	5	47,354
Richmond, Va.	5	52,988
Baltimore, Md.	4	142,106
Jacksonville, Fla.	4	48,196
Montgomery, Ala.	3	29,970
Mobile, Ala.	2	24,514
Shreveport, La.	2	27,219
Charleston, S.C.	2	28,062
Dallas, Tex.	2	38,742
Raleigh, N.C.	1	12,575
Nashville, Tenn.	1	42,836
TOTAL	91	1,121,491

Mean ratio of doctorate recipients to total Negro population   1:12,324

Table 2-8. Cities and towns in which two or more of 459 scientists in this study were born with the ratio of doctorates to 1930 Negro census population given for cities and towns with 3 or more doctorates.

Cities & Towns	No. Doct.	Negro 1930 Census	1 Science doctorate:
1. Brunswick, Ga.	4	6,049	1,512
2. Henderson, N.C.	4	2,843	711
3. Greenville, S.C.	4	10,871	2,718
4. Petersburg, Va.	4	12,600	3,150
5. Greensboro, N.C.	4	14,050	3,513
6. Augusta, Ga.	6	24,190	4,032
7. Boston, Mass.	4	20,574	5,144
8. Houston, Tex.	12	63,337	5,278
9. Portsmouth, Va.	3	18,849	6,283
10. Washington, D.C.	17	132,068	7,769
11. Louisville, Ky.	5	47,354	9,471

12.	Kansas City, Mo.	4	38,574	9,644
13.	Montogomery, Ala.	3	29,970	9,990
14.	Richmond, Va.	5	52,988	10,598
15.	Pittsburgh, Pa.	5	54,983	10,997
16.	Atlanta, Ga.	8	90,075	11,259
17.	Jacksonville, Fla.	4	48,196	12,049
18.	Norfolk, Va.	3	43,942	14,647
19.	St. Louis, Mo.	6	93,580	15,597
20.	New Orleans, La.	7	129,632	18,519
21.	Memphis, Tenn.	5	96,550	19,310
22.	Birmingham, Ala.	5	99,077	19,815
23.	Philadelphia, Pa.	11	219,599	19,964
24.	Detroit, Mich.	4	120,066	30,017
25.	Chicago, Ill.	7	233,903	33,415
26.	Baltimore, Md.	4	142,106	35,527
	New York, N.Y.	7	327,706	46,815
	Mobile, Ala.	2	24,514	
	Macon, Ga.	2	23,158	
	Columbus, Ga.	2	14,157	
	Indianapolis, Ind.	2	43,967	
	Baton Rouge, La.	2	10,675	
	Shreveport, La.	2	27,219	
	New Bedford, Mass.	2	3,631	
	St. Joseph, Mo.	2	4,055	
	Atlantic City, N.J.	2	15,611	
	Camden, N.J.	2	11,340	
	Cincinnati, Ohio	2	47,818	
	Charleston, S.C.	2	28,062	
	Columbia, S.C.	2	19,519	
	Dallas, Tex.	2	38,742	
	N. Little Rock, Ark.	2	19,698	
	Albany, Ga.	2	7,394	
	Opelousas, La.	2	2,858	
	Prentiss, Miss.	2	*	
	Tupelo, Miss.	2	2,284	
	Salisbury, N.C.	2	3,964	
	Rock Hill, S.C.	2	2,410	
	Sumpter, S.C.	2	5,145	
	Kingstree, S.C.	2	1,158	
	Beaumont, Tex.	2	18,551	
	Smithville, Tex.	2	800	
	Navasota, Tex.	2	2,483	
	Gloucester, Va.	2	*	

Table 2-8, cont'd

DeRidder, La.	2	1,255
Williamsburg, Va.	2	854
Roanoke, Va.	2	12,386
Charlotte, N.C.	2	

*not available

3

Undergraduate Origins

Of the 587 persons in this study, undergraduate
origins are known for 586. The 44 schools from which
4 or more of these persons received their undergraduate degrees are presented in Table 3-1 along with the
number who later obtained the doctorate in the bio-
sciences, chemistry, the physical, agricultural, and
pharmaceutical sciences. These 44 colleges and universities are led by Howard (47) and followed by
Morehouse (35), Fisk (21), Tuskegee (20), Southern
(19), Lincoln (Pa.) and Virginia State College (16
each), Hampton (15), and others. Fourteen other
colleges and universities each produced 3 persons,
25 others produced two, while 48 institutions
produced one each for a total of 131 institutions
(see appendix for list). One of the more interesting
features about the undergraduate origins of Negro
science doctorates compared to the total science
doctorate pool is the absence of either of the 20
top-producing universities among the first 10 producers of Negro science doctorates (Table 3-2). The
University of Illinois is closest being number 12 on
the list of these 586 persons followed by the
University of Pittsburgh (#14) and Indiana University
(#15). The geographic locations of undergraduate
and graduate schools which produced 4 or more subjects
in this study are presented in Figure 3-1 from which
it may be seen that the undergraduate institutions
are clustered in the south while the leading graduate
universities are clustered in the midwest.
Almost 72 percent or 421 of the 586 persons
whose undergraduate origin is known received this
degree from predominantly Negro institutions which
account for the pattern illustrated in Fig. 3-1 (see
also Table 3-3). The public and privately supported

23

Table 3-1. The 44 colleges and universities from which 4 or more scientists received their undergraduate degree along with the number who earned doctorates in the various areas.

Schools	Rank	Bio.	Chem.	Phys. Sci.	Pharm.	Agric.	TOTAL
Howard U.	1	25	12	10			47
Morehouse	2	15	13	6	1		35
Fisk U.	3	9	5	6	1		21
Tuskegee	4	7	8	1		4	20
Southern U.	5	10	7			2	19
Lincoln U. (Pa.)	6	10	5	1			16
Virginia State	6	6	3	4	1	2	16
Hampton	8	6	3	1		5	15
Prairie View	9	8	2	1		3	14
Talladega	9	3	3	6	2		14
Illinois	11	6	1	4	1	1	13
N. C. A&T	12	3	3	1		5	12
Lincoln U. (Mo.)	13	2	7	2			11
J. C. Smith U.	14	3	4	2	1		10
Pittsburgh	15	5	2	2			9
Texas Southern U.	15	5	3		1		9
Indiana U.	17	1	3	3	1		8
Morgan	17	2	4	2			8
N. C. Central	17	4	4				8
Tenn. A & I U.	17		4			4	8
Virginia Union	17	4	2	2			8
Xavier U. (La.)	17	3	3		2		8
Ark. AM & N	23	3	1			3	7
Chicago	23	3	3	1			7
Ohio State	23	2	2	2	1		7
Paine	23	1	2	4			7
Wiley	23	2	5				7
Clark College	28	3	2	1			6
Dillard U.	28	2	4				6
Michigan	28	4		2			6
Kansas	28	3	2		1		6
W. Va. State	28	2	4				6
Huston-Tillotson	33	1	4				5
Fla. A & M U.	33	1	4				5
Langston U.	33	2	2			1	5

Table 3-1, cont'd

Wilberforce U.	33	2	1	2			5
Amherst	37	3	1				4
Iowa	37	3		1			4
Iowa State U.	37	2	1			1	4
Livingstone	37	2	1		1		4
Cornell	37	1		1		2	4
Connecticut	37	3	1				4
Spelman	37	4					4
Wayne State U.	37	1	3				4

Table 3-2. The 20 leading baccalaureate sources for U.S. natural science doctorates, 1920-61 (Harmon and Soldz, 1963).

University	No. Doctorates
1. U. Calif., Berkeley	2,227
2. Univ. of Illinois	1,987
3. Univ. of Wisconsin	1,647
4. City College of N.Y.	1,508
5. Cornell Univ.	1,490
6. Mass. Inst. of Technol.	1,472
7. Univ. of Chicago	1,434
8. Univ. of Minnesota	1,377
9. Univ. of Michigan	1,367
10. Harvard Univ.	1,157
11. Ohio State Univ.	1,102
12. Penn. State Univ.	958
13. Purdue Univ.	914
14. Columbia Univ.	862
15. Iowa State Univ.	861
16. Univ. of Washington	773
17. Yale Univ.	760
18. New York Univ.	755
19. Calif. Inst. of Technol.	710
20. U.C.L.A.	699

institutions produced equal percentages of recipients.

The relative efficiency of science doctorate production by the predominantly Negro institutions which produced 4 or more of these subjects is presented in Table 3-4. It can be seen from this Table that Morehouse College was the most efficient producer followed by Talladega, Lincoln University (Pa.), Paine, Fisk, and others.

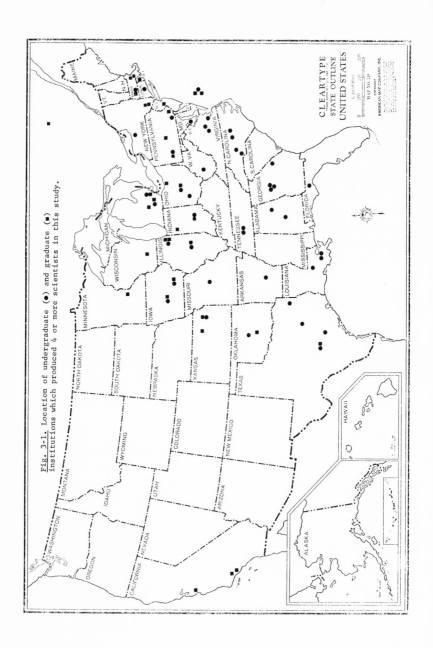

Fig. 3-1. Location of undergraduate (●) and graduate (■) institutions which produced 4 or more scientists in this study.

26

Table 3-3. Summary of undergraduate origins of 586 of the 587 scientists in this study.

	Number	Percentage
Predominantly Negro institutions	421	71.8
Public supported	211	50.1
Private	210	49.9
Other institutions	165	28.2

The efficiency or "production factor" was determined by dividing the number of doctorate recipients by the average class size for the three academic years 1950-51, 1951-52, and 1952-53. These years were selected on the basis of the average age at which the B.S. degree was obtained by these subjects (22 years) assuming birth in 1930 (average "birth year" of subjects in this study). The data for 1950-53 were taken from U.S. office of Education statistics which were not broken down by college or degree areas. It should be borne in mind that universities such as Howard, Southern, and Tuskegee Institute as well as all 17 of the institutions that are land-grant in nature have graduates in areas that normally do not produce many doctorates. These institutions would no doubt have a higher ranking here if only arts and sciences graduates were included for the "production factor" calculations. The total 4-year degree output of these 32 institutions for the six academic years from 1962-63 to 1967-68 is presented in Table 3-5.

The relative percentage of scientists who received their undergraduate training at the predominantly Negro institutions is slightly higher for the 1960-69 doctorate recipients than for all years covered in this study. The institutions from which three or more subjects received the doctorate during this period are indicated in Table 3-5 along with the number of graduates for each school. Southern University produced the highest number (15) of the 221 scientists during this period followed by Morehouse College(15), Howard (12), Tuskegee (12), and others. Of these 221 subjects, 165 or 74.7 percent graduated from a predominantly Negro institution. Fifty-seven percent of these persons graduated from public supported institutions while 43 percent

27

Table 3-4. Relative rate of doctorate production by the predominantly Negro institutions which produced 4 or more doctorates based on the average size of the 1950-53 graduating classes.

Institution	Rank	Av. No. Grads	Prod. Factor[1]
Morehouse	1	104.7	33.42
Talladega	2	56.7	24.69
Lincoln U. (Pa.)	3	81.7	19.58
Paine	4	39.3	17.81
Fisk U.	5	150.7	13.94
Wilberforce U.	6	48.0	10.42
Lincoln U. (Mo.)	7	119.0	9.24
J. C. Smith U.	8	124.7	8.02
Tuskegee Inst.	9	251,3	7.95
Southern U.	10	246.3	7.71
Dillard U.	11	81.0	7.40
Howard U.	12	649.0	7.24
Spelman	13	63.7	6.28
Hampton Inst.	14	245.7	6.11
Livingstone	15	67.0	5.97
Clark College	16	108.3	5.54
Virginia State	17	300.0	5.33
Huston-Tillotson	18	97.7	5.11
Xavier U. (La.)	19	161.0	4.97
Wiley	20	145.0	4.82
Texas Southern U.	21	187.7	4.79
Prairie View	22	307.7	4.54
Virginia Union U.	23	184.0	4.35
Langston U.	24	127.3	3.93
Ark. AM & N	25	179.7	3.89
N. C. Central U.	26	211.3	3.79
N. C. A & T U.	27	337.3	3.55
Morgan State	28	261.0	3.07
Tenn. A & I U.	29	328.7	2.43
Fla. A & M U.	30	340.7	1.47

[1]Determined as follows: number of doctorates/ average graduating class size X 100 = number of doctorates/100 graduates.

Table 3-5. Undergraduate origin of the 221 scientists who received the doctorate between 1960 and 1969.

B. S. Schools	Number
Southern	15
Morehouse	15
Howard	12
Tuskegee	12
Prairie View	7
Virginia State	7
North Carolina A & T	6
Paine	6
Fisk	6
Texas Southern U.	6
Lincoln (Mo.)	6
Morgan	5
Xavier	5
Clark	4
Wiley	4
Wayne State U.	4
Florida A & M	4
Benedict	3
Huston-Tillotson	3
Livingstone	3
Tennessee State	3
Kansas	3
Lincoln (Pa.)	3
South Carolina State	3

Two from each of the following schools: Maryland State, LeMoyne, Morris Brown, Illinois Institute of Technology, Michigan, Central State, Kansas State, Rutgers, University of Connecticut, Rust, Lane, Miles, North Carolina Central.

graduated from private institutions, a lower percentage for these years compared to all years.

Somewhat surprising is the relatively small number of baccalaureate degree recipients from the northern and western colleges and universities in view of current estimates that approximately one-half of Negroes currently in college are attending these institutions. In its report, "Earned Degrees Conferred 1963-64", the U.S. Office of Education reported that 13,533 4-year degrees were awarded by

107 institutions attended predominantly by Negroes.
While the 107 schools were not identified, it is
clear that not all of these graduates were Negro.
On the assumption that approximately 25,000 Negroes
obtain 4-year college degrees per year, about 0.1
percent of this number pursue and receive science
doctorates. Among the 1963-64 graduates cited above,
49 percent received the baccalaureate degree in
education and 16 percent in the social sciences.

With respect to sex of subjects, 90 percent or
529 in this study are males while only 58 or 10
percent are females. These percentages are about the
same for the total U.S. science doctorate pool and
this topic is discussed more fully in Chapter 9. In
spite of the fact that only 10 percent of the subjects
in this study are females, members of this sex comprise
over 50 percent of the number of college graduates
from the predominantly Negro institutions yearly.
For example, for the three academic years 1950-53,
34,672 Negroes graduated from 88 Negro colleges and
universities with only 14,355 or 41.4 percent being
males while 20,317 or 58.6 percent were females, but
yet only 10 percent of the females are represented
in science doctorate fields in this study (Table 3-6).

Table 3-6. Relative number of male and female
graduates from Negro colleges and universities for the
three-year period 1950-1953.

| year | no. schools | number of graduates | | | % males |
		total	males	females	
1950-51	88	12,249	5,709	6,540	46.6
1951-52	87	11,265	4,508	6,757	40.0
1952-53	89	11,158	4,138	7,020	37.1
TOTALS	-	34,672	14,355	20,317	41.4

It can be seen from Table 3-7 that among Negroes,
females continue to graduate from college in larger
numbers than their male counterparts. From these 32
institutions for the six-year period 1962-63 to 1967-
68, 47,083 Negro students graduated of which 43.1
percent were males while 56.9 percent were females
(U.S. Office of Education). This percentage is in
contrast to the national average for the four
academic years from 1961-1964 where females comprised

30

Table 3-7. Total number of undergraduate degrees awarded for the 6 academic years 1962-1968 by the 32 colleges and universities that produced 4 or more science doctorates in this study.

		1962-63			1963-64			1964-65			1965-66			1966-67			1967-68		
		T	M	F	T	M	F	T	M	F	T	M	F	T	M	F	T	M	F
Ala. :	Talladega	35	14	21	63	17	46	97	36	61	67	22	45	53	15	38	75	30	45
	Tuskegee	296	134	162	290	113	177	323	135	188	383	172	211	414	191	223	410	171	239
Ark. :	Ark. AM & N	329	119	210	367	153	214	476	200	276	419	187	232	423	162	261	464	195	269
D.C. :	Howard U.	489	271	218	543	337	206	542	275	267	645	351	294	691	384	307	838	434	404
Fla. :	Fla. A & M	443	190	253	492	196	296	475	179	296	553	246	307	565	226	339	529	224	305
Ga. :	Clark	137	42	95	135	50	85	130	47	83	98	31	67	103	38	65	134	34	100
	Morehouse	124	124	-	122	122		104	104		105	105		119	119		141	141	-
	Morris Brn.	133	49	84	153	46	107	130	42	88	108	29	79	120	26	94	168	51	117
	Paine	50	15	35	53	12	41	48	21	27	65	19	46	58	12	46	67	16	51
	Spelman	100	-	100	113	-	113	94	-	94	102	-	102	99	-	99	172	-	172
La. :	Dillard U.	119	38	81	153	55	98	131	40	91	125	38	87	134	31	103	153	62	91
	Southern U.	625	278	347	728	277	451	773	312	461	788	311	477	974	354	620	947	362	585
	Xavier	115	39	76	112	34	78	99	37	62	111	35	76	121	41	80	180	68	112
Md. :	Morgan	327	152	175	350	173	177	455	216	239	412	182	230	420	189	231	486	180	306
Mo. :	Lincoln U.	200	95	105	195	88	107	217	105	112	235	117	118	241	115	126	225	115	110
N.C. :	J.C. Smith	139	63	76	171	67	104	175	77	98	157	83	74	160	76	84	156	69	87
	N.C. A & T	268	162	106	261	162	99	305	178	127	311	187	124	254	150	104	445	251	194
	N.C. Central	325	109	216	317	132	185	347	130	217	342	129	213	322	109	213	369	119	250
	Livingstone	103	35	68	114	42	72	113	43	70	156	71	85	149	60	89	117	37	80
Ohio :	Wilberforce	43	23	20	65	35	30	45	20	25	66	30	36	72	31	41	101	47	54
Okla.:	Langston U.	111	59	52	135	63	72	128	53	75	138	74	64	135	56	79	162	68	94
Pa. :	Lincoln U.	58	57	1	76	71	5	86	84	2	82	79	3	80	77		88	86	2
Tenn. :	Fisk U.	174	53	121	204	75	129	175	60	115	149	40	109	171	53	118	224	84	140
	Tenn. A & I	503	220	283	480	221	259	457	217	240	538	239	299	504	209	295	410	193	217
Tex. :	Hust.-Tillot.	95	34	61	73	17	56	88	30	58	89	29	60	80	28	52	84	26	58
	Pr. View	300	125	175	353	143	210	394	145	249	395	166	229	430	156	274	414	169	245
	Tex. South.	197	69	128	253	100	153	266	107	159	349	140	209	331	130	201	331	146	183
	Wiley	81	31	50	75	34	41	72	32	40	74	35	39	44	15	29	62	19	43
Va. :	Hampton	218	73	145	248	88	116	257	101	156	263	94	169	274	86	188	366	150	216
	Va. State	318	133	185	331	119	212	476	167	309	234	94	140	213	64	149	267	108	159
	Va. Union	122	46	76	119	55	64	132	44	88	142	60	82	188	69	119	214	83	131
W.Va.:	W.Va. State	176	99	77	224	125	99	209	110	99	251	124	127	235	141	94	215	123	92
Totals:		6753	2951	3802	7368	3222	4146	7819	3347	4472	7952	3519	4433	8177	3413	4764	9014	3861	5153

*Compiled from U.S. Office of Education statistics; T = total; M = males; F = females.

31

41.4 percent of the total of 1,619,047 4-year degree graduates for this period. In spite of outnumbering their male counterparts among college graduates, it is clear that Negro females have not contributed proportionately to the science doctorate pool.
It may wellbe that a higher percentage of Negro females than males is represented in nonscience areas. While females constituted only 6.6 percent of all U.S. natural science doctorates for the period 1920-1961, this sex accounted for 11.7 percent of the nonscience doctorates for the same period (Harmon and Soldz, 1963). The Negro female science doctorate is discussed in Chapter 9.

4

Graduate Origins

The universities from which 4 or more of the 587 subjects in this study earned their doctorate are listed in Table 4-1 along with numbers of persons by degree area. The largest number obtained the doctorate degree from Ohio State University (45) followed by the State University of Iowa and the University of Michigan (36 each), the University of Chicago (30), the University of Illinois (29), Cornell (27), etc. These 37 institutions from which 4 or more subjects earned the doctorate are followed by 7 others from which 3 subjects each earned the doctorate, 12 others from which two each, and 31 others from which only one each earned the doctorate making for a total of 87 different universities (see also appendix section). As a group, the Big-10 universities accounted for 37 percent of the 587 doctorate recipients. This compares with 29 percent of all U.S. natural science doctorates granted by Big-10 universities between 1920 and 1961 (Harmon and Soldz, 1963).

With respect to degree areas, it may be noted from Table 4-1 that a significantly large number of degrees in the physical sciences was obtained from the University of Michigan while the University of Chicago and Wayne State University awarded significantly larger numbers of doctorates in chemistry than any of the other universities. In the biosciences, Ohio State and the State University of Iowa stand out in terms of numbers of degrees granted compared to the other universities.

In regards to doctorate sources by the scientists in this study as compared to the national science doctorate pool, an inspection of Table 4-2 reveals greater similarities in schools of doctorate origin than is the case for baccalaureate sources. Thirteen

33

Table 4-1. The 37 universities from which 4 or more of the 587 scientists earned their doctorate along with the doctorate areas and number from each university.

University	Rank	Bio.	Chem.	Physical	Pharm.	Agric.	Total
Ohio State	1	23	8	4	1	9	45
Iowa	2	26	6	2	2		36
Michigan	2	14	4	15	3		36
Chicago	4	12	12	4	2		30
Illinois	5	14	5	4	2	4	29
Cornell	6	10	6	5		6	27
Michigan State	7	10	4			7	21
Wisconsin	7	12	6	1	1	1	21
Penn. State	9	10	6	2		1	19
Howard	10	8	7	2	1		18
Pennsylvania	10	8	5	5			18
Wayne State	12	3	13		1		17
Iowa State	13	7	7	1	1		16
Catholic U.	14	8	2	5			15
Harvard	15	8	2	3			13
Pittsburgh	15	5	5	3			13
Minnesota	17	4	3	2		1	10
Purdue	17	3	5	1	1		10
Texas	19	1	6	2			9
New York U.	19	3	2	4			9
Indiana	21	2	5	1			8
Brown	22	5	2				7
Kansas	22	2	5				7
Massachusetts	22	1	1			5	7
Oklahoma	22	4	2	1			7
Rutgers	22	3	1			3	7
Calif. Tech.	27		4	2			6
Case West. Res.	27	4	2				6
Kansas State	27	3	3				6
Mass. Inst. Tech.	27		1	5			6
Ill. Inst. Tech.	27		2	4			6
Columbia	32	2	3				5
Georgetown	32	2	2	1			5
California	34		2	1	1		4

Table 4-1, cont'd

McGill	34	4		4
South. Calif.	34	3	1	4
Yale	34	2	2	4

Table 4-2. The 20 leading U.S. institutions in the production of natural science doctorates for the period 1920-1961 compared by rank order to the doctorate origins of the 587 scientists in this study. (Harmon and Soldz, 1963).

University	National rank	Rank for subjects in this study
U. of Wisconsin	1	7
U. of Illinois	2	5
Cornell U.	3	6
U. Calif., Berkeley	4	*
Mass. Inst. Tech.	5	27
U. of Michigan	6	2
U. of Minnesota	7	17
U. of Chicago	8	4
Ohio State U.	9	1
Columbia U.	10	32
Harvard U.	11	15
Iowa State U.	12	13
Purdue U.	13	17
Yale U.	14	34
Johns Hopkins U.	15	**
Stanford U.	16	**
State U. of Iowa	17	2
Princeton U.	18	0
Penn. State U.	19	9
U. of Pennsylvania	20	10

*Only 2 doctorates; **Only 1 doctorate each

of the 20 leading universities in this study are among the leading 20 nationally. The notable exceptions are Michigan State, Wayne State, Howard, and Catholic Universities which rank 7, 11, 13, and 14, respectively, among the subjects in this study while they were not among the 20 leading natural science doctorate universities nationally for the years 1920-1961. Among the latter universities, Columbia, Johns Hopkins, Princeton, Stanford, and the University of California (Berkeley) are low producers of science

35

doctorates in this study.

The 221 recipients of science doctorates
between 1960-1969 received their degrees from 70
institutions including 26 from which three or more
graduated (Table 4-3). This list is led by Howard
University (17) followed by Michigan (16), Ohio State
(14), and Wayne State University (12). For the
period in question, Big-10 universities accounted for
only 30 percent of these degrees while universities
in the south (Howard not included) accounted for 23
or 10.4 percent. This compares with 28 or 4.8 percent for all years covered by this study. Among
these are universities which enforced racial segre-
gation prior to the Supreme Court decision of 1954.
Five of the 27 unconfirmed doctorate recipients not
included in this study are alledged to have received
their degrees from one or more of these institutions,
all since 1960.

The degree areas in which the science doctorates
for all subjects were awarded are compared to
recipients since 1960 and are presented in Table 4-4.
Some 42.9 percent or 252 of the subjects were awarded
their degrees in the biological and medical sciences
which include all areas of botany, zoology, bacteriology, public health, pathology, anatomy, and related
areas (see Chapter 5 for a further breakdown of bio-
science fields). Of the 214 receiving doctorates
since and including 1960, 104 or 48.6 percent were
in this field, a slight increase for the latter
years. Chemistry recipients make up 31.7 percent or
186 of all of the doctorate recipients and this area
includes analytical, organic, inorganic, physical,
radiation, biochemistry, and related specialities.
Seventy or 33 percent of the more recent graduates
received their degrees in chemistry which is approximately the same percentage for all years. The
physical sciences, including all phases of mathematics,
physics, astronomy, meteorology, geology, and engineering (chemical, electrical, engineering science,
mechanical, and metallurgical), are represented by 94
or 16 percent of all subjects. The agricultural
sciences are represented by 38 or 6.5 percent while
17 or 2.9 percent of the subjects were awarded
doctorates in the sciences of pharmacy. While the

Table 4-3. Doctorate origin of the 221 scientists
who received this degree between 1960 and 1969.

Ph. D. School	Number
Howard	17
Michigan	16
Ohio State	14
Wayne State U.	12
Iowa	9
Catholic U.	9
Michigan State U.	8
Penn. State	8
Wisconsin	8
Texas	7
Purdue	7
Illinois	7
Oklahoma	6
New York U.	5
Minnesota	4
Chicago	4
Kansas State	4
Kansas	4
Ill. Inst. Tech.	4
Univ. of S. Calif.	4
Georgetown	4
Rutgers	3
New Hampshire	3
W. Va. U.	3
Brown	3

Two from each of the following schools: Indiana,
Cornell, Mass. Inst. Tech., Calif. Inst. Tech.,
Berkeley, Pittsburgh, Massachusetts, Oregon, U. of
Conn.
One each from 35 other schools.

percentage concentration by the more recent recipients
in chemistry and the other physical sciences is about
the same as for all years covered, the percent of
those receiving degrees in the agricultural sciences
since 1960 dropped sharply to only 4 of the 214 or
1.9 percent compared to 6.5 percent for all years.
The latter category includes agronomy, horticulture,
animal science, dairy technology, and other related
specialties. The 17 persons representing the

pharmaceutical sciences obtained degrees in pharmacology, pharmacognosy, pharmaceutical chemistry, and related areas.

The undergraduate feeder pattern for baccalaureate institutions that produced 6 or more doctorates reveals no outstanding pattern in terms of a "preferred" doctorate university except in cases where the undergraduate source is also a potential doctorate source (see appendix Table A-5, pp. 75-82).

Table 4-4. Degree areas in which the 587 doctorates earned their degrees compared to those who earned degrees between 1960-1969.

Areas	1876-1969		1960-1969	
	No.	Percent	No.	Percent
Bio-sciences	252	42.9	104	48.6
Chemistry	186	31.7	70	32.7
Physical sci.	94	16.0	32	14.9
Agricultural sci.	38	6.5	4	1.9
Pharmaceutical	17	2.9	4	1.9

5

The Bio-sciences

The bio-sciences are by far the largest broad area represented by the persons in this study. Almost 43 percent of the 587 persons received doctorates in this area compared to the national average of 37.9 for the years 1920-1961. The states in which 235 of the 252 were born are indicated in Table 5-1. The leading states of origin are Texas and South Carolina (24 each), Virginia (22), Louisiana and Georgia (21 each), North Carolina (20), Alabama (15), Pennsylvania (14), and the District of Columbia (11). All total, 24 states and territories produced two or more scientists while 4 other U.S. states, Puerto Rico and the French West Indies produced one each. The 10 leading states accounted for 181 or 77 percent of bio-scientists. In terms of north-south patterns, 81 percent of these scientists were born in a southern state with the Atlantic and Gulf Coast states leading all others.

A further breakdown of the 252 bio-scientists by degree fields is presented in Table 5-2. Sixty percent of these persons received their doctorates in one of the zoological sciences which included anatomy, cytology, endocrinology, entomology, genetics, parasitology, physiology, and related disciplines. Over 18 percent were awarded doctorates in bacteriology or microbiology while 13 percent received degrees in the botanical sciences. General biology was indicated by 21 or 8.3 percent while a total of 7 or almost 3.0 percent hold degrees in pathology, public health, medical science, and surgery. Only 4 of the subjects hold doctorates in nutrition and all are females.

Table 5-1. Birth states of scientists who received
doctorates in the bio-sciences.

States	Number
South Carolina	24
Texas	24
Virginia	22
Georgia	21
Louisiana	21
North Carolina	20
Alabama	15
Pennsylvania	14
District of Columbia	11
Mississippi	9
Missouri	6
Tennessee	5
Florida	4
Illinois	4
West Virginia	4
Arkansas	3
Kentucky	3
Maryland	3
New Jersey	3
New York	3
Ohio	3
British West Indies	3

Table 5-2. Degree fields represented by the 252
bio-science doctorates.

Fields	Number	Percent
Zoological sciences	141	55.9
Bacteriology	46	18.3
Botany & Mycology	33	13.1
General Biology	21	8.3
Medical[1]	7	2.8
Nutrition	4	1.6

[1]Include 3 in pathology and one each in public health,
medicine, medical science, and surgery.

The undergraduate origins of the 252 scientists
in this group are summarized in Table 5-3. Twenty-
nine colleges and universities produced three or
more, 20 produced two, while 45 other institutions
produced one bio-science doctorate each. Howard

University leads all of the 94 different institutions
with 25, followed by Morehouse College with 15,
Southern and Lincoln (Pa.) Universities each with 10.
The predominantly Negro institutions produced 180 or
71.4 percent of these scientists with the private
schools accounting for close to one-half.

The doctorate origins of persons in the bio-
sciences are presented in Table 5-4. A total of 59
institutions are represented here with 27 producing
three or more scientists, 4 producing 2, while 28
other universities produced one each. The State
University of Iowa leads all other universities with
26 followed by Ohio State University with 23, the
Universities of Michigan and Illinois with 14 each,
the Universities of Chicago and Wisconsin with 12
each, and Cornell, Penn. State, and Michigan State
Universities with 10 each. From the Big-10 universities, 108 or 43 percent of these persons obtained
their doctorates which is a higher percentage for the
bio-sciences than for chemistry or the other physical
sciences.

With respect to Negro firsts in the bio-sciences,
Alfred O. Coffin became the very first American
Negro to obtain a bio-science doctorate when Illinois
Weselyn University conferred this degree upon him
in 1889. Coffin's degree was awarded in zoology
and, of course, was the first for this academic
discipline. The next doctorate recipient in this
area was Charles H. Turner who was awarded this degree
in 1907 by the University of Chicago. Julian Lewis
was the first to be awarded the doctorate in physiology, having been awarded this degree in 1915 by
the University of Chicago. The first in anatomy was
Roscoe McKinney (U. of Chicago, 1930); the first in
botany was Jessie Jarue Mark (Iowa State U., 1935);
first in pathology was Robert Jason (U. of Chicago,
1932); first in nutrition was Flemmie P. Kittrell
(Cornell, 1936); and the first in public health
(Dr. P.H.) was Paul B. Cornely (U. of Michigan, 1934).
It may be noted from this list of firsts that Negroes
chose the more prestigious universities prior to
around 1940 for science doctorates. These universities
established early reputations for accepting Negroes
for graduate work before most of the other major

41

Table 5-3. Undergraduate origins of bio-science doctorates.

Schools	Number
Howard U.	25
Morehouse	15
Lincoln U. (Pa.)	10
Southern U.	10
Fisk U.	9
Prairie View A & M	8
Tuskegee Inst.	7
Illinois	6
Virginia State	6
Hampton	6
Pittsburgh	5
Texas Southern U.	5
Michigan	4
N. C. Central U.	4
Spelman	4
Virginia Union U.	4
Clark	3
Connecticut	3
Arkansas AM & N	3
J. C. Smith U.	3
Morris Brown	3
Talladega	3
N. C. A & T U.	3
Kansas	3
Amherst	3
Chicago	3
Iowa	3
South Carolina State	3
Xavier U. (La.)	3

Two each from Shaw U., Rutgers U., Lane, Miles, Wilberforce, Benedict, Livingstone, Langston, Lincoln U. (Mo.), Morgan State, Md. State, Texas College, Leland, Ohio State U., Iowa State U., Syracuse U., Wiley, West Va. State, Bates, and Dillard U. and one each from 47 other institutions.

American universities. It may be noted here that Negroes seeking doctorates in all fields prior to around 1920 showed a clear preference for certain foreign universities. Indeed, the very first American Negro to receive a Ph.D. degree was Father Patrick

Healy who was awarded this degree in 1865 by the University of Louvain in Belgium (Bond, 1967).

Table 5-4. Institutions from which biological and medical scientists received their doctorates.

Schools	Number
State U. of Iowa	26
Ohio State U.	23
Michigan	14
Illinois	14
Chicago	12
Wisconsin	12
Cornell	10
Michigan State U.	10
Penn. State U.	10
Catholic U.	8
Howard U.	8
Harvard U.	8
Pennsylvania	8
Iowa State U.	7
Brown U.	5
Pittsburgh	5
Case-Western Reserve	4
Oklahoma	4
Minnesota	4
New York U.	3
Kansas State U.	3
New Hampshire	3
Purdue U.	3
Rutgers U.	3
U. of Southern Calif.	3
Wayne State U.	3
West Virginia U.	3

Two each from Indiana U., Kansas, Columbia U., and the U. of Conn. and one each from 28 other institutions.

The general type of employment held by the bioscientists in this study is indicated in Table 5-5 based upon information available during the early part on 1970 or upon last known addresses. In the case of deceased persons, their last place of employment was recorded. This type of information was available for 229 of the 252 persons. Over 88

percent or 203 of these scientists were employed
by academic institutions with 79.3 percent or 161
of these being employed by the predominantly Negro
institutions. Slightly over 4 percent were employed
by industry, 3.5 percent by the federal government,
while 8 or 3.5 percent of the 229 were in miscellaneous endeavors including 3 in hospital staff
positions, two housewives, etc.

Table 5-5. Last known employment status of 229 of
the 252 bio-science doctorates.

Employment	Number	Percent
Academic Institutions	203	88.6
Predominantly Negro	161	79.3
Industry	10	4.3
Government	8	3.5
Miscellaneous	8	3.5

6

Chemistry & The Pharmaceutical Sciences

The 186 chemists and 17 pharmaceutical scientists are treated together in this Chapter because of the general similarities between these disciplines.

The states of birth for 183 of the 186 chemists are presented in Table 6-1 from which it can be seen that Alabama led all others with 19 followed closely by Texas with 18, North Carolina with 17, Georgia with 13, Virginia with 9, and Louisiana and South Carolina with 8 each. All together, 31 U.S. states are represented in addition to Panama, Cuba, the Virgin Islands, and the British West Indies. The 19 leading states accounted for 106 or 58 percent of the 183 for whom states of birth are known. The southern states produced 125 or 68 percent. This percentage is lower than the 81 percent for bio-scientists who were born in the south.

Undergraduate origins are known for all 186 of these scientists and it can be seen from Table 6-2 that Morehouse College which produced 13 led all others followed closely by Howard University with 12, Tuskegee with 8, and Southern and Lincoln (Mo.) Universities with 7 each. A total of 80 different colleges and universities are represented among the undergraduate origins with 25 institutions producing three or more, followed by 10 which produced two each and 45 which produced one each. Of the 186, 130 or 70 percent graduated from predominantly Negro colleges and universities. This percentage is basically the same as that for the bio-scientists in the previous chapter.

The 186 chemists received their doctorate degrees from a total of 61 different universities with Wayne State University leading all others with 13 followed by the University of Chicago with 12, Ohio State

University with 8, and Howard and Iowa State
Universities with 7 each (Table 6-3). A total of
23 universities produced three or more doctorates in
chemistry followed by 16 which produced two each and
22 others which produced one each. While the Big-10
universities accounted for 43 percent of the bio-
scientists in the previous chapter, only 46 or 24.7
percent of the chemists received their doctorates
from Big-10 universities.

Table 6-1. Birth states of chemistry doctorates.

States	Number
Alabama	19
Texas	18
North Carolina	17
Georgia	13
Virginia	9
Louisiana	8
South Carolina	8
Kentucky	7
Pennsylvania	7
Illinois	6
Missouri	6
Michigan	6
New Jersey	6
New York	6
District of Columbia	5
Florida	5
Massachusetts	5
Mississippi	4
Tennessee	4
Kansas	3
Maryland	3

Two each from Calif., Indiana, Okla., and B. W. I.,
and one each from Ark., Del., Cuba, Conn., Minn.,
Ohio, Panama, Wisc., W. Va., and Virgin Islands.

The first American Negro to receive a doctorate
in chemistry was Saint Elmo Brady who was awarded
the Ph.D. in 1916 by the University of Illinois. The
following year, Edward Chandler became the second
recipient of this degree which was awarded also by
the same university.

Table 6-2. Undergraduate origins of chemistry doctor-ates.

Schools	Number
Morehouse	13
Howard U.	12
Tuskegee Institute	8
Southern U.	7
Lincoln U. (Mo.)	7
Fisk U.	5
Lincoln U. (Pa.)	5
Wiley	5
Dillard U.	4
Huston-Tillotson	4
W. Va. State	4
J. C. Smith U.	4
Florida A & M U.	4
N. C. Central U.	4
Morgan State	4
Tennessee A & I U.	4
N. C. A & T U.	3
Hampton Inst.	3
Talladega	3
Texas Southern U.	3
Indiana U.	3
City College of N. Y.	3
Wayne State U.	3
Virginia State	3
Chicago	3

Two each from Clark, Knoxville, Paine, Va. Union,
Prairie View, Langston, Ohio State U., Kansas,
Pittsburgh, and Cincinnati, and one each from 45
other institutions.

The type of employment held by 184 of the 186
chemists in this study is indicated in Table 6-4
based upon the latest available information or last
known addresses. It can be seen that 121 or 65.8
percent of these persons held academic positions with
95 or 78.5 percent of these being in the predominantly
Negro institutions. While only around 4 percent of
the bio-scientists were employed by industry, over 23
percent of the chemists held this type of employment.
Sixteen or 8.7 percent held federal government
positions while 4 or slightly over 2 percent were in

miscellaneous endeavors. One of the 15 listed as holding federal employment was U.S. Air Force Capt. Robert H. Lawrence, Jr. who was a NASA astronaut at the time of his death during the latter part of 1967. Lawrence was awarded the Ph.D. in physical chemistry in 1965 by Ohio State University. The miscellaneous category includes one medical practitioner, one housewife, one hospital employee, and one welfare rights organization official.

Table 6-3. Institutions from which chemists received their doctorates.

Institutions	Number
Wayne State U.	13
U. Chicago	12
Ohio State U.	8
Howard U.	7
Iowa State U.	7
Cornell U.	6
U. Texas	6
Penn. State U.	6
Iowa	6
Wisconsin	6
Illinois	5
Indiana	5
Kansas	5
Pennsylvania	5
Pittsburgh	5
Purdue U.	5
Michigan	4
Michigan State	4
Calif. Inst. Tech.	4
McGill U.	4
Columbia U.	3
Kansas State U.	3
Minnesota	3

Two each from Harvard, Brown, Catholic U., U. Calif., Oklahoma, U. of Wash., Georgetown U., Case West. Res., Washington U., Cincinnati, Syracuse, Delaware, Illinois Inst. Technol., New York U., Washington State U., Brooklyn Polytechnical Inst. and one each from 22 others.

With respect to the 17 pharmaceutical scientists, states of birth are known for 14. Ten of these were born in a southern state while 10 or 62.5 percent obtained the baccalaureate degree from a predominantly Negro institution. Ten of the 17 received the Ph.D. from a Big-10 university.

In regards to the type of employment held by the pharmaceutical scientists, 12 were known to be employed by academic institutions with 8 being in predominantly Negro colleges and universities. At least three of these individuals also hold the M.D. degree while four are females. Most are pharmacologists with pharmacognosy, pharmacy, and pharmaceutical chemistry being represented among the 17. Arnold H. Maloney became the first Negro to receive a doctorate in this area when the University of Wisconsin conferred upon him the Ph.D. in 1931.

Table 6-4. Last known employment status of 184 of the 186 chemists.

Employment	Number	Percent
Academic institutions	121	65.8
Predominantly Negro	95	78.5
Industry	43	23.4
Government	16	8.7
Miscellaneous	4	2.2

7

The Physical Sciences

The physical science represented in this study other than chemistry consist of mathematics, physics, engineering, geology, astronomy, and meteorology (Table 7-1). Of the 94 persons in this group, 75 received doctorates in mathematics and physics. Among the 12 engineers are persons in chemical, civil, electrical, metallurgical, engineering mechanics, mechanical, and related areas. Only two American Negroes are known to have ever obtained doctorates in astronomy and only one in meteorology.

Table 7-1. Degree fields of the 94 physical science doctorates other than chemists.

Fields	Number	Percent
Mathematics	41	43.6
Physics	34	36.2
Engineering	12	12.8
Geology	4	4.2
Astronomy	2	2.1
Meteorology	1	1.1

The states in which 84 of these persons were born are indicated in Table 7-2 from which it can be seen that Georgia with 12 holds a clear lead over the other 24 states. Fifty-seven of 84 or 67.9 percent of these individuals were born in one of the southern states. This percentage is essentially the same as that for the chemists in this study but somewhat lower than for the bio-scientists.

The undergraduate origins of these scientists are presented in Table 7-3 from which it can be seen that Howard produced 10 and Talladega, Fisk, and Morehouse each produced 6. Only 51 or 54 percent of these persons graduated from the predominantly Negro institutions compared to 70 percent for chemists and 71.4 percent for bio-scientists. The private institutions produced 66.7 percent of the 51 physical science doctorates who graduated from the predominantly Negro institutions.

Table 7-2. Birth states of scientists who received doctorates in the physical sciences other than chemistry.

States	Number
Georgia	12
Virginia	8
Alabama	6
Illinois	6
South Carolina	6
Pennsylvania	5
Missouri	5
Texas	5
Kentucky	4
Florida	3
Indiana	3
Louisiana	3
New Jersey	3

Two each from Maryland, Oklahoma, Tennessee, and West Virginia, and one each from 7 other states.

Table 7-3. Institutions from which the doctorate recipients in physical sciences other than chemistry earned their first degree.

Institution	Number
Howard	10
Fisk	6
Morehouse	6
Talladega	6
Illinois	4
Paine	4
Virginia State	4
Ill. Inst. Tech.	3
Indiana	3
Mass. Inst. Tech.	3

Two each from the following: J.C. Smith, Va. Union, Lincoln (Mo.), Morgan, Temple, Mich., Wilberforce, Ohio State, and Pittsburgh. One each from 27 others.

Physical science doctorates were obtained from
a total of 45 different universities with the University of Michigan being clearly out front of the
others with 15 (Table 7-4), Cornell University,
M.I.T., Catholic U., and the University of Pennsylvania
follow with 5 each. Just why the University of
Michigan is so conspicuous in this area is not clear.
The Big-10 universities as a group accounted for 30
percent of persons in this area compared to 43
percent of bio-scientists and only 24.7 percent of
chemists.

Table 7-4. Institutions from which doctorate recipients
in the physical sciences other than chemistry
received their doctorates.

Institutions.	Number
Michigan	15
Cornell	5
Catholic U.	5
Mass. Inst. Technol.	5
Pennsylvania	5
Chicago	4
Illinois	4
Ill. Inst. Technol.	4
N. Y. Univ.	4
Ohio State	4
Harvard	3
Pittsburgh	3

Two each from Minnesota, Iowa, Texas, Yale, Howard,
Cal. Tech., and Penn. State and one each from 19
others.

With respect to Negro doctorate firsts in the
physical sciences, Elbert Cox became the first in
mathematics when Cornell University conferred the
Ph.D. upon him in 1925. As was stated in Chapter 1,
Edward A. Bouchet became the very first American
Negro to receive a science doctorate and the first
in physics when Yale University conferred the Ph.D.
upon him in 1876. The second Negro to receive a Ph.D.
in this area was Elmer Imes who was awarded this
degree in 1918 by the University of Michigan. George
M. Jones became the first Negro doctorate recipient
in engineering in 1925 when the University of

Michigan conferred this degree upon him in the area
of civil engineering. The only two Negroes known
to hold doctorates in astronomy are Harvey W. Banks
(Georgetown University,1961) and Benjamin Peery
(University of Michigan, 1962), while Charles E.
Anderson is the only known doctorate holder in
meteorology (M.I.T., 1960). Marguerite Thomas became
the first Negro to obtain the Ph.D. in geology when
Catholic University awarded her this degree in 1942.

The type of employment held by 88 of the 94
persons in this category is indicated in Table 7-5.
Seventy-one or 81 percent of these being employed
by the predominantly Negro institutions. Nearly 14
percent were employed by industry while only 4.5
percent were employed by federal governmental agencies.
One member of this group (a mathematician) is a
black Muslim minister.

Table 7-5. Last known employment status of 88 of the
94 persons in the physical sciences other than
chemistry.

Employment	Number	Percent
Academic Institutions	71	80.7
Predominantly Negro	42	47.7
Industry	12	13.6
Government	4	4.5
Other	1	1.1

The type of employment available to Negroes in
the physical sciences today is in sharp contrast to
that available to Bouchet after he received his
doctorate. In spite of the fact that he was elected
to Phi Beta Kappa during his senior year at Yale
and ranked #6 in his graduating class of 1874,
Bouchet spent nearly all of his postdoctoral years
teaching in high schools. From 1876 to 1902, he
taught physics and chemistry in the Institute for
Colored Youth, Philadelphia, Pa. The following year,
he taught physics and mathematics at Sumner High
School in St. Louis, Mo. For the next three years,
he served as U.S. Inspector of Customs at the
Louisiana Purchase Exposition in St. Louis. He
served at St. Paul Normal and Industrial School,

53

Lawrenceville, Va., from 1906 to 1908 at which time he was made principal of the Lincoln High School in Gallipolis, Ohio. He died on October 28, 1918 at the age of 66 in New Haven, Conn. where he was born (Negro History Bull., Vol. 31, No. 8, Dec., 1968). While Bouchet did not teach on the college or university level, he was employed in the teaching profession. In 1943, Greene (1946) found that 96 percent of all Negro doctorate holders had at one time or another taught in a Negro college or university. Of the 13.6 percent of physical scientists employed by industry, most of them taught briefly in a Negro institution before entering industry.

8

The Agricultural Sciences

The agricultural sciences are represented in this study by agronomy, horticulture, animal husbandry, field crops, dairy technology, and related areas. Of the 38 persons in these areas, states of birth are known for only 28. These 28 were born in 12 different states with North Carolina producing 5 followed by Virginia with 4, and Louisiana, Mississippi and Texas with 3 each (Table 8-1). With respect to north-south origins, all but one of these persons were born in the south (96.4 percent), a percentage considerably higher than that for any of the other degree areas represented by the 587 subjects in the study.

Table 8-1. Birth states of scientists who received doctorates in the agricultural sciences.

States	Number
North Carolina	5
Virginia	4
Louisiana	3
Texas	3
Mississippi	3
Arkansas	2
Oklahoma	2
Tennessee	2

One each from Alabama, Florida, Kansas, and Kentucky.

Undergraduate origins are known for 37 of the 38 agricultural scientists, and it can be seen from Table 8-2 that these 37 received their undergraduate training at 16 different colleges and universities with Hampton Institute leading the others with 5 followed by North Carolina A & T, Tennessee A & T, and Tuskegee with 4 each. Thirty-two or 86.5 percent of

these persons received their undergraduate degrees
from a predominantly Negro institution with the
private Negro institutions producing considerably
fewer than their public-supported counterparts.
This relatively low percentage output of agricultural
scientists by the private schools is to be expected
since most of these are basically liberal arts type
institutions.

Table 8-2. Schools from which the doctorate recipients
in the agricultural sciences received their undergraduate training.

B. S. Schools	Number
Hampton	5
North Carolina A & T	4
Tennessee State	4
Tuskegee	4
Arkansas AM & N	3
Prairie View	3

Two each from the following schools: Southern, Va.
State, Cornell, Alcorn A & M. One each from 6 other
schools.

These 38 individuals received their doctorates
from only 9 different universities with Ohio State
the leader with 9, followed by Michigan State with 7
and Cornell with 6 (Table 8-3). The Big-10 universities produced 59.4 percent of these persons, a
percentage higher than for any of the other degree
areas represented in this study.

George Spaulding became the first Negro doctorate
holder in the agricultural sciences when Massachusetts
State College conferred the Ph.D. upon him in 1935.
While dairy technology is listed as belonging among
the agricultural sciences, only one Negro is known to
hold a Ph.D. in this field, this person being
Emmett Bassett who was awarded the degree in 1954 by
Ohio State University.

In regards to type of employment held by 37 of
these persons, 35 or 94.6 percent held academic
positions with 34 or 97.1 percent of these being
employed by the predominantly Negro institutions.
One was employed by a governmental agency and only 1
by industry (Table 8-4). All 38 of the agricultural

56

scientists are males and only two are known by the author to be deceased.

Table 8-3. Institutions from which agricultural scientists received their doctorates.

Ph.D. School	Number
Ohio State U.	9
Michigan State U.	7
Cornell	6
Massachusetts	5
Illinois	4
Rutgers	3

One each from the following institutions: Minnesota, Wisconsin, Pennsylvania State.

Table 8-4. Last known employment status of 37 of the 38 agricultural scientists.

Employment	Number	Percent
Academic Institutions	35	94.6
Predominantly Negro	34	97.1
Industry	1	2.7
Government	1	2.7

As may be expected, the agricultural scientists employed by the predominantly Negro institutions were at one or more of the 17 of these institutions which continue their land-grant status. While there is a national trend towards a reduction in doctorates in this area, the changing patterns in agriculture in the south as well as the broadening of coverage by the predominantly white land-grant universities both account for the decrease in numbers of Negro doctorates in these fields.

9

The Negro Female Science Doctorate

Special attention is devoted to the Negro
female science doctorate recipient because of the
relatively low numbers of females at this level in
view of the fact that more Negro females graduate
from college than Negro males (see Chapter 3). Fifty-
eight or around 10 percent of all subjects in this
study are females, and it can be seen from Table 9-1
that they were born in 22 different states with
North Carolina leading others with 8, followed by
the District of Columbia with 7, Georgia with 6,
and Texas with 5. Of the 52 for whom states of
birth are known, 40 or 77 percent were born in the
south.

Table 9-1. Birth states of 52 of the 58 female
doctorate recipients.

States	Number
North Carolina	8
District of Columbia	7
Georgia	6
Texas	5
Pennsylvania	4
Virginia	4
Louisiana	2
South Carolina	2

One each from Alabama, California, Illinois, Missouri,
Mississippi, Maryland, New Jersey, New York, Michigan,
Ohio, Florida, Jamaica, Tennessee, and West Virginia.

Undergraduate origins are known for 57 of these
58 females, and Table 9-2 presents the leading
schools which show Howard University clearly at the
top with 12. Spelman College and Tuskegee Institute
follow with 4 each. All total, these 57 persons

obtained their undergraduate degrees from 36
different colleges and universities. The predominantly
Negro institutions produced 37 or 63.8 percent of
these, a percentage lower than the average for this
study. In her study of 412 Negro female college
graduates in six cities, Noble (1956) found that 71
percent were graduates of Negro colleges or universities,
a percentage slightly higher than that for the
subjects in this study.

Table 9-2. Undergraduate origins of 57 of the 58
female doctorates in this study.

Schools	Number
Howard U.	12
Spelman	4
Tuskegee	4
N. C. Central U.	3
Hampton Inst.	2
Wayne State U.	2

One each from 30 other schools.

The 58 females obtained their doctorates from 35
different universities with Cornell, Howard, Michigan,
and Pennsylvania State Universities having produced
4 each (Table 9-3). Only 13 or 22.4 percent obtained
their doctorates from the Big-10 universities, a
percentage lower than the average for all subjects in
this study. Twenty-five of the 58 (43 percent)
received the doctorate between 1960-1969 and accounted
for 11.3 percent of the total of 221 for these years.

Table 9-3. Doctorate origins of the 58 females.

Institutions	Number
Cornell U.	4
Michigan	4
Howard U.	4
Penn. State U.	4
Chicago	3
Iowa State U.	3
Ohio State U.	3
Wayne State U.	3

Two each from Catholic U., U. of Illinois, and U.
of Wisconsin, and one each from 24 others.

Table 9-4 presents the degree areas represented by the 58 females. Over 50 percent obtained the doctorate in the bio-sciences followed by 12 or 20.7 percent in chemistry, and 6 or 10.3 percent in mathematics. Of the bio-science degree disciplines, 14 are represented by the zoological sciences, 7 each by bacteriology and botany, and 3 by general biology. Not represented among the females are doctorates in the agricultural sciences, engineering, or physics.

Table 9-4. Doctorate fields of the 58 females.

Fields	Number	Percent
Bio-science	31	53.4
Chemistry	12	20.7
Mathematics	6	10.3
Nutrition	4	6.9
Pharmaceutical sci.	4	6.9
Other	1	1.7

With respect to degree fields, the first Negro female to receive a doctorate in bacteriology was Ruth E. Moore (Ohio State University, 1933). The first in nutrition was Flemmie P. Kittrell (Cornell, 1936); first in botany was Jessie Jarue Mark (Iowa State University, 1935); first in zoology was Roger Arliner Young (University of Pennsylvania, 1940), while Ruth Lloyd was the first in anatomy (Western Reserve University, 1941). Apparently the first Negro females to receive the Ph.D. in mathematics were Evelyn Boyd Collins (Yale, 1949) and Majorie Browne (Michigan, 1949) while Marie M. Daly was apparently the first in chemistry (Columbia, 1947).

The employment status of 55 of the 58 females is presented in Table 9-5 from which it can be seen that 44 or 75.9 percent held academic positions with 33 or 75 percent of these being in the predominantly Negro institutions. Four each or 6.9 percent were employed by industry and the federal government while 3 were housewives.

While there was a national decrease in the percentage of female science doctorates from 10.8 for 1920-24 to only 5.2 for 1960-61 (Harmon and Soldz, 1963), there appears to be an increase in the percentage of Negro female doctorates in the natural sciences. The national mean percentage for female science doctorates between 1920 and 1961 is 6.6 while in this study females comprise 10 percent of the 587 scientists. Of interest is the fact that 23 or 41.1 percent of these obtained the doctorate during and since 1960. In its summary reports on American science manpower for 1966 and 1968, the National Science Foundation found that 8 percent of 242,763 scientists who were registered in 1966 were females while in 1968 females constituted 9 percent of 297,942. The registrants in these surveys included scientists at all degree levels. Nevertheless, the data may indicate a national trend towards more Negro females entering the sciences.

Table 9-5. Last known employment status of 55 of the 58 females in this study.

Employment	Number	Percent
Academic Institutions	44	75.9
Predominantly Negro	33	75.0
Industry	4	6.9
Government	4	6.9
Housewives	3	5.2

10

Epilogue

One of the more basic questions which may be raised over the findings presented herein is the following: Why have not more northern-born Negroes contributed to the science doctorate pool? Also, why are the predominantly Negro colleges and universities more prominent as Negro science doctorate producers than other colleges and universities? Both of these questions are difficult to answer but some of the possible explanations follow.

1. Southern Negroes have in the past been educated by other Negroes who, while sometimes deficient in academic preparation and lacking proper physical facilities, gave their all to their students and instilled into them the desire and motivation to go on and do well. Too, the existence of places of employment in the south in the form of the Negro colleges and universities no doubt serve as motivational forces for youngsters growing up in the area. Of the 299 U.S. cities and towns in which 459 of these scientists were born, 117 or 25.5 percent were born in one of the 37 locations of a predominantly Negro college or university. In other words, these 37 locations which represent 12.4 percent of the 299 accounted for over 25 percent of the doctorates in this study. The Negro student at a Negro college or university who is taught by science doctorates and who sees Negro deans and college or university presidents generally feels some assurance for job security if he or she obtains a doctorate. This same pattern does not hold in the north even though Negroes may be found on science faculties in quite a few of the northern colleges and universities. The tendency here is for the persons in question to remain rather obscure in the Negro community and even when their presence on the faculty of such

institutions is known, many Negroes in the community
tend to treat this as an exceptional feat and
consequently do not readily make the assumption that
they, too, may be employed in one of the sciences
at such institutions if they should make the proper
preparations. The employment pattern of Negro
science doctorates tends to make this rather clear.
Since few of the predominantly Negro colleges and
universities are located in the north, the motivational role these institutions apparently serve for
southern Negroes will have to be assumed by either
northern colleges and universities, or by industry.
Unfortunately, this picture is brightening only
slightly.
    2. It has been stated often that the northern
Negro has economic opportunities which the southern
Negro does not have and consequently does not need
to obtain doctorate degrees in order to make a
decent living. The generally low salaries which
many colleges and universities offer make the notion
of seeking a doctorate rather unattractive to some
northern Negroes who can sometimes earn just about
as much without higher degrees. Just how valid
this notion is as well as some of the many others
which one hears as "explanations" for the dilemma
in question, is difficult to know. It may be noted
that social conditions in many and most large
northern cities in the past several years certainly
do not make for the type of atmosphere or environment
that is needed for excellence in the sciences. It
is the opinion of the author that fewer and fewer
Negro science doctorates will come from the larger
northern cities in the immediate future unless
some special efforts are made to acquaint northern
Negroes more fully with the potential opportunities
that exist in these areas and demonstrate to them
that employment is a reality upon the acquisition of
the science doctorates in whatever field they
desire to enter and wherever they choose to become
employed. This view has already been expressed (Jay,
1968).
THE PAST AND THE FUTURE
    While it is the view of the author that it
would be premature to ask about and speak of the

accomplishments of American Negro science doctorates since well over 80 percent of all such persons are yet alive, it should be noted that some outstanding achievements have been made by this group in a relatively short period of time. While no American Negro has ever won a Nobel Prize in the sciences, at least one has been appointed to membership in the National Academy of Sciences (a mathematician), several served on the Manhattan Project which led to the development of the atomic bomb, several have and continue to serve on editorial boards of major scientific publications in their fields, several have and continue to serve as consultants to both the federal government and industry, several hold key positions in industrial and research complexes, etc. The achievements of this segment of the science doctorate pool has to be considered outstanding when one considers the many adversities which this group has faced over the years and continues to face individually and collectively. One should also consider that approximately 8 out of 10 of the persons in this group is employed by the academic institutions in this country which are in the worst position of most all such institutions to provide research time and facilities. The current interest in Negro faculty members by the larger and more prestigious universities of the country is a healthy sign for all sides. The continuing improvements in the quality of academic life by the predominantly Negro institutions is also healthy for the future of Negro science doctorates. With the proper emphasis at all levels beginning with young Negro students in elementary school and in the home and continuing throughout the graduate training years and subsequent employment, this relatively large and untapped source of scientific manpower can be made more viable for the good of the individuals involved, their institutions, their cities and states, and the country as a whole.

References.

Bond, Horace M. 1967. A study of factors involved
    in the identification and encouragement of
    unusual academic talent among underprivileged
    populations. Project No. 5-0859, Contract No.
    SAE 8028, Office of Education, U.S. DHEW.
Greene, Harry W. 1946. Holders of Doctorates Among
    American Negroes. (Boston: Medor Publishing
    Company).
Harmon, L. R. 1961. High school backgrounds of
    science doctorates. Science 133; 679-688.
Harmon, L. R. and Soldz, H. 1963. Doctorate Production
    in United States Universities 1920-1962. Nat'l
    Acad. Sci., Nat'l Res. Coun. Pub. No. 1142.
Jay, James M. 1968. Michigan Negro science doctorates.
    pp. 46-47 Michigan Challenge, June, 1968.
    (Michigan State Chamber of Commerce Publication).
Noble, Jeanne L. 1956. THE NEGRO WOMAN'S COLLEGE
    EDUCATION. Teachers College, Columbia University
    (New York, N.Y.).
Taylor, Julius H. 1955. THE NEGRO IN SCIENCE. Morgan
    State College Press.

Appendix Tables

Cities and towns in which only one scientist in this study was known to be born.

ALABAMA
  Livingston
  Anniston
  Camden
  Selma
  Sipsey
  Huntsville
  Beatrice
  Tuskegee
  Athens
  Greenville
  Evergreen
  Boligee
  Linden
  Brighton
  Nymph
  Alexandria
  Talladega
  Bessemer
  Calhoun
  Gadsden
  Ramer

ARKANSAS
  Dermott
  Gurdon
  College Heights
  Millville
  Wabash

CALIFORNIA
  Berkeley
  Oakland

FLORIDA
  High Springs
  Palatka
  Bartow
  Apalachilla
  West Palm Beach
  Tallahassee
  Gainesville

GEORGIA
  Elberton
  Dublin
  Quitman
  Mayfield
  Talbotton
  Madison
  Dawson
  Roberta
  Hawkinsville
  Athens
  Whitesburg
  Pavo
  Tyerly
  Bainbridge
  Waycross
  Arlington
  Fitzgerald
  Thomasville

ILLINOIS
  Shawneetown
  St. Louis
  Edwardsville
  Springfield
  Centralia
  Alton

INDIANA
  Evansville
  Gary
  Bloomington
  Madison

KANSAS
  Newton
  Fort Scott
  Iola

KENTUCKY
  Monticello
  Lancaster

KENTUCKY, CONT'D
  Bowling Green
  Danville
  Lexington
  Berea
  Hopkinsville
  Shelbyville

LOUISIANA
  Gray
  Abbeville
  Minden
  Baker
  Ethel
  Port Hudson
  Benston
  Galin
  Lake Charles
  Alexandria
  Oak Grove
  Big Bend
  Hoston
  Curtiss
  Greensburg
  Columbia

MASSACHUSETTS
  Pittsfield

MARYLAND
  Annapolis
  Snow Hill
  Macon
  Cumberland

MICHIGAN
  Paw Paw
  Vandalia

MISSISSIPPI
  Vicksburg
  Friarspoint

66

Indianola	NEW JERSEY	Union
Woodville	Pennsauken	Great Falls
Alcorn	Whitesboro	Chesterfield
Lexington	Elizabeth	Lancaster
Canton	Flemington	Abbeville
Newton	Bayonne	Dalzell
Cary	Cape May	Williamston
Clarksdale		Spartanburg
	NEW YORK	Florence
MISSOURI	Buffalo	Bennetsville
Independence	New Rochelle	Bucksport
Syracuse	Brooklyn	Bishopville
New Madrid		Gaffney
	OHIO	Trenton
NORTH CAROLINA	Columbus	
Elizabeth City	Youngstown	TENNESSEE
Rowland		Nashville
Seven Springs	OKLAHOMA	Whitehaven
Wilmington	Muskogee	Rock Island
Lumberton	Wewkoka	Murfreesboro
Bayboro	Enid	Millington
Winston Salem	Bison	Chapel Hill
Asheville	Bennington	Arlington
Rockingham	Chandler	Chattanooga
Four Oaks	Fallis	
Jamesville	Weleetak	TEXAS
Welton		Henderson
Wilksboro	PENNSYLVANIA	New Waverly
Raleigh	Frazier	Jacksonville
Harelsville	Montrose	Plano
Gastonia	Westchester	Deweyville
Sanford	Sharpsburg	Amarillo
Sedalia	Jenkintown	Valley Mills
Tryon	Langhorne	Itasca
Reidsville		Crockett
Oxford	SOUTH CAROLINA	Thunder
Clarkston	Kershaw	Gonzales
Hartford	Saltens	Oakland
Concord	Orangeburg	Vernon
Statesville	Anderson	Waco
Duplin County	Eastover	Palestine

67

Table A-1, Cont'd

Falls County

San Antonio

Mexia

Cedar Creek

Celina

Georgetown

Lee County

Geneva

Tyler

Ft. Ringold

Woodville

WEST VIRGINIA

  Institute

  Hiawatha

  Kimball

  Huntington

  Charleston

  Wheeling

VIRGINIA

  Manchipongo

  Middleburg

  Salem

  Winchester

  Denniston

  Christiansburg

  Victoria

  Boyce

  Hampton

  Northfolk

  Falls Church

  Charlottesville

  Danville

  Emporia

  Appomattox

  Goochland Cty.

  Martinsville

  Alexandria

  Pocahontas

  Fairfax

Tappahannock

Farmville

CONNECTICUT

  New Haven

MINNESOTA

  St. Paul

WISCONSIN

  Milwaukee

CUBA

  Camaguey

PANAMA

  Colon

PUERTO RICO

  Santurce

BRITISH W. INDIES

  Barbados

68

Table A-2. Baccalaureate schools which produced less than 4 of the subjects in this study.

Schools	A*	B*	C*	D*	E*	Total
Morris Brown	3					3
Benedict	2	1				3
Texas College	2		1			3
Bates	2	1				3
Knoxville College	1	2				3
Ill. Inst. Technol.			3			3
M.I.T.			3			3
Alcorn A & M	1			2		3
Univ. of Calif.		2	1			3
Atlanta Univ.	1	1	1			3
S. C. State	3					3
City College of N.Y.		3				3
Rutgers Univ.	2		1			3
Shaw Univ.	2	1				3
Maryland State	2					2
Leland College	2					2
Syracuse Univ.	2					2
Univ. of Cincinnati		2				2
Temple Univ.			2			2
Univ. of Penn.	1				1	2
Tougaloo College	1	1				2
Savannah State	1			1		2
Alabama A & M		1		1		2
Western Mich. Univ.	1	1				2
Central State (Ohio)	1	1				2
Harvard Univ.	1	1				2
LeMoyne (Tenn.)		1	1			2
Claflin College	1	1				2
Yale		1	1			2
Univ. of Minnesota	1		1			2
Rust College	1		1			2
Tufts College	1	1				2
Univ. of Colorado	1	1				2
Kansas State Univ.	1			1		2
Lane College	2					2
Miles College	2					2
McGill Univ.	1	1				2
Trinity College	1	1				2
Oberlin College		1			1	2

Table A-2, Cont'd.

	1	2	3	4	Total
Univ. of W. Va.	1				1
Bennett College	1				1
Columbia Univ.			1		1
West Indies Univ.				1	1
Ky. State College	1				1
Penn. State Univ.	1				1
Univ. of Rhode Island		1			1
Springfield	1				1
Roosevelt Univ.		1			1
Grambling College		1			1
Northwestern Univ.		1			1
Rennslaer Poly.		1			1
Berea College		1			1
Univ. of Nebraska	1				1
Bluefield State	1				1
Bryn Mawr	1				1
Ill. State Normal		1			1
Dartmouth	1				1
Bradley Univ.		1			1
St. Augustine (N.C.)	1				1
U.C.L.A.		1			1
Creighton Univ.	1				1
Duquesne Univ.		1			1
Queens College		1			1
College of N. Rochelle	1				1
Villanova	1				1
D. C. Teachers	1				1
Ohio Wesleyen	1				1
Mt. Holyoke	1				1
DePaul Univ.		1			1
Friends Univ.		1			1
Brooklyn Poly.			1		1
Case Univ.			1		1
Allen Univ.			1		1
Miner Teachers			1		1
Boston Univ.			1		1
Univ. of Arizona			1		1
Drexel Inst.			1		1
Smith College			1		1
Mich. State Univ.	1				1
Kent State Univ.	1				1
Shippensburg		1			1

70

Calif. Inst. Technol.		1		1
Alabama State College	1			1
Waynesburg	1			1
Phila Col. Pharm.			1	1
Wittenberg			1	1
St. Andrews Univ.	1			1

A=Bio-sciences; B = Chemistry; C = Physical sciences other than chemistry; D = Agricultural sciences; E = Pharmaceutical sciences.

Table A-3. The 4-year predominantly Negro Colleges and Universities in the U. S. and the number of undergraduate degrees awarded for the 1967-1968 academic year.

Institutions	Location	No. Degrees
Alabama A & M	Huntsville	298
Alabama State	Montgomery	339
Albany State	Albany, Ga.	168
Alcorn A & M	Alcorn, Miss.	365
Allen Univ.	Columbia, S. C.	172
Arkansas AM & N	Pine Bluff	231
Barber-Scotia	Concord, N. C.	76
Benedict	Columbia, S. C.	271
Bennett	Greensboro, N.C.	113
Bethune-Cookman	Daytona Beach, Fla.	202
Bishop College	Dallas, Texas	127
Bluefield State	Bluefield, W. Va.	107
Bowie State	Bowie, Md.	100
Central State	Xenia, Ohio	425
Cheyney State	Cheyney, Penn.	278
Claflin College	Orangeburg, S. C.	162
Clark College	Atlanta, Ga.	134
Coppin State	Baltimore, Md.	85
Delaware State	Dover	127
Dillard Univ.	New Orleans, La.	153
Edward Waters	Jacksonville, Fla.	225
Elizabeth City	Elizabeth City, N.C.	196
Fayetteville St.	Fayetteville, N.C.	124
Fisk Univ.	Nashville, Tenn.	224
Florida A & M	Tallahassee	529

Florida Memorial	St. Augustine	77
Fort Valley St.	Fort Valley, Ga.	281
Grambling College	Grambling, La.	386
Hampton Inst.	Hampton, Va.	366
Howard Univ.	Washington, D. C.	838
Huston-Tillotson	Austin, Texas	84
Jackson State	Jackson, Miss.	380
Jarvis Christian	Hawkins, Texas	65
Johnson C. Smith	Charlotte, N. C.	156
Kentucky State	Frankfort	151
Knoxville College	Knoxville, Tenn.	123
Lane College	Jackson, Tenn.	146
Langston Univ.	Langston, Okla.	162
LeMoyne College	Memphis, Tenn.	135
Lincoln Univ.	Jefferson City, Mo.	225
Lincoln Univ.	Lincoln Univ., Penn.	88
Livingstone	Salisbury, N. C.	117
Maryland State	Princess Ann	101
Miles College	Birmingham, Ala.	129
Mississippi Indust.	Holly Springs	79
Morehouse	Atlanta, Ga.	141
Morgan State	Baltimore, Md.	486
Morris College	Sumpter, S. C.	80
Morris Brown	Atlanta, Ga.	168
Norfolk State	Norfolk, Va.	285
N. C. Central	Durham, N.C.	369
N. C. A & T	Greensboro, N. C.	445
Paine College	Augusta, Ga.	67
Paul Quinn	Waco, Texas	55
Oakwood College	Huntsville, Ala.	56
Philander Smith	Little Rock, Ark.	99
Rust College	Holly Springs, Miss.	129
St. Augustine's	Raleigh, N.C.	114
St. Paul's Poly.	Lawrenceville, Va.	76
Savannah State	Savannah, Ga.	229
Shaw Univ.	Raleigh, N. C.	117
South Carolina St.	Orangeburg	227
Southern Univ.*	Baton Rouge, La.	947
Spelman College	Altanta, Ga.	172
Stillman College	Tuscalosa, Ala.	108
Talladega College	Talladega, Ala.	75

Tennessee A & I	Nashville	410
Texas College	Tyler	63
Prairie View A & M	Prairie View, Tex.	414
Texas South. Univ.	Houston	331
Tougaloo College	Tougaloo, Miss.	103
Tuskegee	Tuskegee Inst., Ala.	410
Virginia State	Petersburg	267
Virginia Union	Richmond	214
West Va. State	Institute	215
Wilberforce Univ.	Xenia, Ohio	101
Wiley College	Marshall, Texas	62
Winston-Salem St.	Winston-Salem, N.C.	207
Voorhees College	Denmark, S. C.	46
Xavier Univ.	New Orleans, La.	180

Compiled from U. S. Office of Education Statistics.
Data not available for those not listed.
*All campuses.

Table A-4. Doctorate institutions which produced fewer than 4 scientists in this study.

Institutions	A	B	C	D	E	Total
Univ. New Hampshire	3					3
Univ. Cincinnati		2	1			3
W. Va. Univ.	3					3
Wash. State Univ.	1	2				3
Syracuse Univ.	1	2				3
Univ. of Delaware	1	2				3
Univ. of Conn.	2	1				3
Univ. of Washington		2				2
Washington Univ.		2				2
Northwestern Univ.	1		1			2
Univ. of Rochester	1	1				2
Notre Dame	1	1				2
Stanford Univ.	1	1				2
Univ. of Colorado	1	1				2
Univ. Calif., Berk.		1	1			2
Boston Univ.		1	1			2
Brooklyn Poly.		2				2
U.C.L.A.	1		1			2
Univ. of Oregon	1		1			2

Table A-4, Cont'd.

Institution	A	B	C	D	E	Total
Loyola (Chic.)				1		1
Johns Hopkins			1			1
Ohio Univ.		1				1
Univ. of W. Ontario		1				1
Univ. of Ill.(Chic.)		1				1
St. Louis Univ.		1				1
Univ. of Maryland			1			1
Univ. of Virginia			1			1
Univ. of Georgia			1			1
Yeshiva Univ.			1			1
Ill. Wesleyen	1					1
St. Andrews Univ.	1					1
Bryn Mawr	1					1
Univ. of Toronto	1					1
Emory Univ.	1					1
Radcliffe	1					1
U. Calif., S.Barb.	1					1
Tulane Univ.	1					1
Univ. Libre (Fr.)	1					1
Fordham Univ.	1					1
Univ. of Edinburgh	1					1
Alfred Univ.		1				1
Univ. of Nebraska		1				1
Univ. of Buffalo		1				1
Marquette Univ.		1				1
Adelphi Univ.		1				1
Univ. of Vienna		1				1
Univ. of Akron		1				1
Univ. of Missouri		1				1
Univ. of N. Carolina	1					1
Oregon State Univ.	1					1

A = Bio-sciences; B = Chemistry; C = Physical sciences other than chemistry; D = Agricultural sciences; E = Pharmaceutical sciences.

Table A-5. Doctorate sources of graduates of the 32 undergraduate institutions known to have produced 6 or more scientists in this study.

Grad. Schools	A	B	C	D	E	Total
HOWARD UNIVERSITY (47)						
Howard Univ.	5	1				6
Ohio State U.	2					2
Penn. State Univ.	2	1				3
Wisconsin	2		1			3
Michigan	1	1	1			3
Univ. Penn.	1		2			3
Harvard	2					2
Chicago		2				2
Catholic Univ.			2			2
Cornell Univ.	1	1				2
Univ. Illinois	2					2
Univ. Libre	1					1
Iowa State Univ.	1					1
Stanford Univ.	1					1
Univ. So. Calif.	1					1
Univ. Toronto	1					1
Northwestern Univ.	1					1
Fordham Univ.	1					1
Columbia Univ.		1				1
Washington Univ.		1				1
McGill		1				1
Univ. Pittsburgh		1				1
Univ. of Akron		1				1
Indiana Univ.		1				1
Georgetown Univ.			1			1
Univ. of Virginia			1			1
M.I.T.			1			1
Johns Hopkins Univ.			1			1
MOREHOUSE COLLEGE (35)						
State U. of Iowa	5	1				6
Ohio State Univ.	2		2			4
Minnesota	2		1			3
Chicago	1	1		1		3
Wisconsin	2					2
Howard Univ.		2				2
Calif. Technol.		2				2

Institution	1	2	3	4	Total
Syracuse Univ.	1				1
Brown	1				1
Georgetown Univ.	1				1
Kansas State Univ.		1			1
Univ. of Penn.		1			1
Catholic Univ.		1			1
Univ. of Kansas		1			1
Univ. Calif., Berkeley		1			1
Unif. of Calif.		1			1
Wayne State Univ.		1			1
M.I.T.			1		1
Michigan			1		1
U. C. L. A.			1		1

FISK UNIVERSITY (21)

Institution	1	2	3	4	Total
State Univ. Iowa	3		1		4
Michigan			3		3
Iowa State Univ.		2			2
Univ. of Penn.	1				1
Notre Dame	1				1
Univ. of Texas	1				1
Michigan State U.	1				1
Ohio State Univ.	1				1
Ill. Wesleyen	1				1
Illinois		1			1
Syracuse Univ.		1			1
Marquette Univ.		1			1
Catholic Univ.			1		1
Loyola Univ. (Chic.)			1		1
New York Univ.			1		1

TUSKEGEE INSTITUTE (20)

Institution	1	2	3	4	Total
Howard Univ.		1	1		2
Ohio State Univ.				2	2
Wisconsin	1			1	2
Iowa State Univ.		2			2
Michigan State				1	1
Massachusetts	1				1
Washington St. U.	1				1
Pittsburgh	1				1
Purdue Univ.	1				1
Univ. of Penn.	1				1

	1	2	3	4	Total
Univ. of Kansas	1				1
Wayne State Univ.		1			1
Penn. State Univ.		1			1
Syracuse Univ.		1			1
Univ. of Oklahoma		1			1
Univ. of Chicago			1		1

SOUTHERN UNIVERSITY (19)

	1	2	3	4	Total
State Univ. Iowa	4				4
Univ. of N. Hampsh.	3				3
Michigan State	1	1		1	3
Purdue Univ.		2			2
Univ. of Oklahoma	1				1
Ohio State Univ.		1			1
Catholic Univ.	1				1
Alfred Univ.		1			1
Univ. of Nebraska		1			1
Univ. of Washington		1			1
Cornell Univ.				1	1

LINCOLN (PA.) UNIVERSITY (16)

	1	2	3	4	Total
Univ. of Penn.	2	2	1		5
Penn. State Univ.	1	1			2
Catholic Univ.	2				2
Harvard	1				1
Chicago	1				1
Michigan	1				1
Columbia	1				1
W. Va. Univ.	1				1
West. Ontario		1			1
Delaware		1			1

VIRGINIA STATE COLLEGE (16)

	1	2	3	4	Total
Michigan State	3			1	4
Wisconsin	1	1			2
Howard Univ.			1	1	2
New York Univ.	1				1
Harvard	1				1
Univ. of Penn.		1			1
Cornell		1			1
Catholic Univ.			1		1
Univ. Cincinnati			1		1

Table A-5, Cont'd.

Penn. State U.			1		1
Massachusetts				1	1

HAMPTON INSTITUTE (15)

Cornell	1	1	1	2	5
Michigan State		1		2	3
Ohio State Univ.	2				2
Iowa State Univ.	2				2
Iowa	1				1
Washington St. U.		1			1
Massachusetts				1	1

TALLADEGA (14)

Michigan	1		2		3
Pittsburgh		1	1		2
Minnesota			2		2
Howard Univ.	1				1
Brown	1				1
Iowa		1			1
Columbia		1			1
New York Univ.			1		1
Univ. of Calif.				1	1
Illinois				1	1

UNIV. OF ILLINOIS (13)

Illinois	4	1	2	1	8
Chicago	1				1
Wisconsin	1				1
Harvard			1		1
Ill. Inst. Technol.			1		1
Penn. State Univ.				1	1

PRAIRIE VIEW A & M (14)

Ohio State Univ.	2			3	5
Kansas State Univ.	1	1			2
Iowa	1				1
Minnesota	1				1
Iowa State Univ.	1				1
Cornell	1				1
Illinois	1				1
Georgetown		1			1
Univ. Calif., Berk.			1		1

78

NORTH CAROLINA A & T (12)

Michigan State	1			1	2
Massachusetts				2	2
Iowa	1				1
Catholic Univ.	1				1
Wisconsin		1			1
Penn. State Univ.		1			1
Univ. of Conn.		1			1
New York Univ.			1		1
Illinois				1	1
Rutgers				1	1

LINCOLN (MO.) UNIV. (11)

Illinois	1			1
Michigan	1			1
Washington Univ.		1		1
Ill. Inst. Technol.		1		1
Missouri		1		1
Univ. Ill. (Chic.)		1		1
Chicago		1		1
Western Reserve		1		1
Univ. of So. Calif.		1		1
M. I. T.			1	1
Cornell			1	1

JOHNSON C. SMITH UNIV. (10)

State U. of Iowa		2	1	3
Chicago	1	1		2
Wisconsin	1			1
Illinois	1			1
Pittsburgh		1		1
Catholic Univ.			1	1
Michigan			1	1

PITTSBURGH (9)

Pittsburgh	2	1	1	4
Cornell	1	1		2
Michigan	1			1
Iowa	1			1
Boston Univ.			1	1

TEXAS SOUTHERN (9)

Iowa	2	1		1	4
Univ. of Texas		2			2
Brown	1				1
Purdue	1				1
Univ. of So. Calif.	1				1

INDIANA UNIV. (8)

Indiana Univ.		3	1		4
Iowa	1				1
Cornell			1		1
Michigan			1		1
Chicago				1	1

MORGAN STATE (8)

Univ. of Penn.	1	1		2
Wayne State Univ.		2		2
Penn. State Univ.	1			1
Howard Univ.		1		1
Univ. of Maryland			1	1
Illinois			1	1

N. C. CENTRAL (8)

Michigan	1		1
Harvard	1		1
Connecticut	1		1
Wayne State Univ.		1	1
Wisconsin		1	1
Calif. Inst. Tech.		1	1
Univ. of Buffalo		1	1
Cornell	1		1

TENNESSEE A & I (8)

Minnesota		1	1	2
Illinois		1	1	2
Rochester		1		1
Adelphia Univ.		1		1
Cornell			1	1
Michigan State			1	1

VIRGINIA UNION (8)

Iowa	1	1
Catholic Univ.	1	1
Michigan	1	1

	1	2	3	4	5	Total
St. Andrews Univ.	1					1
Chicago		1				1
Iowa State Univ.		1				1
Harvard			1			1
Penn. State			1			1
XAVIER (LA.) UNIV. (8)						
Wayne State Univ.		1		1		2
Michigan State	1					1
Penn. State Univ.	1					1
Illinois	1					1
Indiana Univ.		1				1
Notre Dame		1				1
Purdue				1		1
ARKANSAS AM & N (7)						
Ohio State Univ.					2	2
Wisconsin	1					1
Iowa	1					1
Yale	1					1
Iowa State Univ.		1				1
Cornell					1	1
UNIV. OF CHICAGO (7)						
Chicago	2	1	1			4
Edinburgh	1					1
Univ. of St. Louis		1				1
Catholic Univ.		1				1
OHIO STATE (7)						
Ohio State Univ.	2	2	1	1		6
Michigan			1			1
PAINE COLLEGE (7)						
Ohio State Univ.	1					1
Michigan		1				1
Minnesota		1				1
Univ. of Georgia			1			1
Oklahoma State Univ.			1			1
Chicago			1			1
Yeshiva Univ.			1			1

Table A-5, Cont'd.

WILEY COLLEGE (7)

	A	B	C	D	E	Total
Chicago		2				2
Wisconsin	1					1
Penn. State Univ.	1					1
Boston Univ.		1				1
Cornell		1				1
Massachusetts		1				1

CLARK COLLEGE (6)

	A	B	C	D	E	Total
Cornell	1					1
West Va. Univ.	1					1
Howard Univ.	1					1
Chicago		1				1
Wayne State Univ.		1				1
Northwestern Univ.			1			1

DILLARD (6)

	A	B	C	D	E	Total
Michigan	1					1
Ohio State		1				1
Minnesota	1					1
Cincinnati		1				1
Brown		1				1
Washington Univ.		1				1

UNIV. OF KANSAS (6)

	A	B	C	D	E	Total
Univ. of Kansas	1	1				2
Michigan	1			1		2
Minnesota		1				1
Rutgers	1					1

UNIV. OF MICHIGAN (6)

	A	B	C	D	E	Total
Univ. of Michigan	2		2			4
Illinois	1					1
Rochester	1					1

WEST VIRGINIA UNIV. (6)

	A	B	C	D	E	Total
Iowa	1					1
Chicago	1					1
Penn. State Univ.		1				1
Wayne State Univ.		1				1
Ohio State Univ.		1				1
Brooklyn Poly.		1				1

A = Bio-sciences; B = Chemistry; C = Physical sciences;
D = Pharmaceutical sciences; E = Agricultural sciences.

82

Cover letter sent to scientists whose biographies
were unpublished.

WAYNE STATE UNIVERSITY
Department of Biology
Detroit, Michigan 48202

1965

Dear Dr.

I am in the process of completing a study of
Negroes who hold the Ph.D., Sc.D, or Dr. P. H. degree
in the sciences, engineering, and mathematics, and
would like a few moments of your time in completing
and returning to me the enclosed information sheet.
For your convenience, I am enclosing a stamped, self-
addressed envelope for your use. Rest assured that
the information asked for will be used only in a
statistical sense and will not be associated with you
by name. When the study is completed, I shall be
pleased to inform you as to its source.

Your time and attention to this request will be
highly appreciated.

Sincerely yours,

James M. Jay

Encls.

Questionnaire sent along with letter on previous page.

NEGRO DOCTORATES IN THE SCIENCES

Name _____
       last   first   initial

Date of birth _____. Place of birth ____
          mo.   day   yr.

_____. High School from which
   city and state

you graduated _____, City & State _____

_____. Size of your graduating class: less

than 50 /____/; between 100 & 200 /____/; over 200 /____/.

College or university from which you graduated

_____. Year of graduation _____. School

from which you received the doctorate _____,

year _____. Ph.D. field _____.

Your present position and address _____,

_____.

List below any honors and/or awards received by you

for scientific work in your field.

RETURN TO: Dr. James M. Jay
           Department of Biology
           Wayne State University
           Detroit, Michigan 48202

Index

85